OLIVER HAZARD PERRY

Books by Alfred H. Fenton

DANA OF THE SUN

OLIVER HAZARD PERRY

This book has been manufactured in accordance with the paper conservation orders of the War Production Board.

Oliver Hazard Perry

by

Alfred H. Fenton

Illustrated by Gordon Hake

Farrar & Rinehart, Inc.
New York   Toronto

TO

MY MOTHER

CONTENTS

OLIVER HAZARD PERRY

A Seaworthy Name

CAPTAIN CHRISTOPHER RAYMOND PERRY STOOD BY THE living room window, looking out into the front yard. He was facing southeast and if it hadn't been for the knoll in front of the house he would have been able to see Point Judith and Long Island Sound.

If he only could get a glimpse of the water he might be able to think better. Why couldn't the Perrys have put the house on higher land where a man could see the ocean? Afraid of a little wind, probably. Quakers didn't even want to fight nature. Well, if there was any thinking to be done that day, it would have to be done in sight of the ocean. Captain Perry turned on his heel and made for the front door. He walked as though the floor were rolling and pitching under his feet.

"Where are you going, Christopher?" his mother asked from her rocking chair by the other window.

"Out to think," was the reply, and, pushing aside the gauze screen that was draped over the front door, he stepped out into the yard.

It was hot in the sun, but not so hot as it would have been if a strong southwest wind had not been blowing.

Captain Perry strode down the path toward the knoll. Once he got sight of Point Judith he could concentrate.

Point Judith, as treacherous a point as any on the coast. It didn't look particularly treacherous this hot August afternoon in 1785. True, the wind was kicking up a few whitecaps, but it had to come from the opposite direction to bring trouble. Southwesters were good, steady breezes—smoky sou'westers some people called them, because of the haze that usually accompanied them. A man could run to Newport in no time in a breeze like that and then wear ship and run right up Narragansett Bay to Providence.

Christopher Perry stood with his hands behind his back and scanned the horizon. Only one sail could he see and that one not very clearly. It looked like that of a schooner standing out to sea. Then he brought his gaze nearer at hand. The post road from Providence to New York crossed his path. Looking southward on it he saw a cloud of dust. Stagecoach most likely. That was the only sign of life, other than the sail, that he could see. Point Judith Pond, which lay directly in front of him, was not being troubled much by the wind.

Satisfied that everything was as it should be, Perry settled down to the problem at hand. There was a baby in the house that had to have a name. It was his first baby and it was a son at that.

"Be a lot easier to name a ship," Perry said aloud.

A ship was graceful, like a tern; a baby was

just so many spars and ribs that someday might become beautiful or even useful. Still, if there was a
chance that he might become a captain, a good captain, he should have a fitting name. Maybe he should
be named for Captain James Nicholas of the *Trumbull*. There was a fighter. Would have licked the

British letter of marque *Watt*, too, if the *Trumbull's*
masts hadn't fallen when they did.

Trouble was the rest of the family wasn't so
keen about the sea, and fighting. There would have
to be a compromise. If only more of the Perrys and
the Hazards had been seamen, the problem wouldn't
be so hard, but most of them had been landowners,
yes, and even slaveowners. Take old Oliver Hazard

there, he had had a regular plantation just like the ones in the South, but then most of the big landowners in Rhode Island had owned slaves at one time or another. Some still did, although they were fast being liberated. And it wasn't entirely out of the goodness of their owners' hearts, like people said. There just wasn't need for slaves in Rhode Island any more.

There were several reasons for the change. In the first place, the big landowners had lost their profitable trade with the West Indies, for while the United States had gained their freedom from Great Britain, they had been barred from trading with England's other colonies.

Newport and other New England cities had been hit badly even before the Revolution. The compound profit of the triangular trade with Africa and the West Indies had been pinched off by the mother country. No longer did New England ships trade rum for slaves in Africa, slaves for molasses in the West Indies, and molasses for rum in New England.

But the sea was going to come back into its own. You just wait and see. American merchants already were looking for other ports. It was a risky but profitable trade they were finding. There was no navy to protect American merchantmen, so they had to look out for themselves, especially in the Mediterranean where the Barbary pirates from Algiers, Morocco, Tunisia, and Tripoli held forth.

Christopher Perry's thoughts were interrupted by the fact that the schooner he had been watching had come about and was now standing in toward Point Judith. He kept his eye on her for a moment and then resumed his musing.

Of course, he could give in to the rest of the family and let them name the child whatever they wanted because there undoubtedly would be more sons. Only if this one turned out to be a captain, it would be a shame if he had to carry some silly family name to sea.

The only thing to do was compromise, find some name that represented the sea as well as the family. He'd go back and talk it over with his mother. He took one last look at the ocean and then retraced his steps.

As soon as he entered the house, he spoke:

"Mother, I have been thinking of a name for this son of mine and I have come to the conclusion that he should be named—"

"Oliver Hazard Perry," his mother interrupted. "After your brother who died at sea two years ago and after your grandfather."

Christopher Perry mouthed the name a few times and then patted his mother's hand. "A good idea," he said. "That takes care of the sea and the family at the same time."

CHAPTER TWO

An Odd School

CAPTAIN PERRY MOUNTED THE NARROW, STEEP STAIRway which led from the living room to the upstairs bedroom in which his wife and his newly born son lay. He opened the bedroom door gently and, seeing that his wife was awake, stepped inside the room. His wife turned her head toward him and smiled.

"I've just had a talk with Mother," Perry began, "about a name for our son and she wants it to be Oliver Hazard Perry, after the boy's uncle and great-grandfather." Perry covered his wife's hand with his. "I led her to believe that that would be the name we would accept, for while we are living with Father and Mother I think it wise to be diplomatic. There will be other children. In fact, I'm inclined to believe that in due time we'll need all the names in your family plus all those in mine."

Perry's wife smiled. "I like the name," she said. "I like it because I like your grandfather. He has always been so kind to me."

"I like the name too," said Perry. "It reminds me of Captain Oliver Reed who helped me get out of the prison ship *Jersey*. But that's the start of a yarn and you need rest." Perry kissed his wife, paused for a moment to admire his son, and then quietly returned downstairs.

Perhaps their next child would be a girl, he thought, as he entered the living room again. They could name it Sarah Wallace Perry after its mother. He started pacing the floor. Time enough to worry about that when the daughter was born. Meanwhile a man had to think about making a living.

"For goodness sake, sit down," his mother said. "You make me nervous."

"I'm nervous myself," he said, taking a chair. "This sitting around with nothing to do is getting under my skin."

"There is plenty to be done around the farm."

"Yes, I suppose so, but I want to get back to sea. A captain should be able to make himself a tidy sum one of these days, especially if that East Indies trade develops. I think I'll go to Newport tomorrow."

"But what about your wife and child? You can't just up and leave them. I think it's high time you settled down and found yourself a position at home instead of gallivanting all over the globe."

"There's nothing for me to do here. The days of the plantation are gone. Look at your father's property. It's nothing compared to what it used to be. He's lucky that he isn't just starting out the way I am."

Mrs. Perry could see that her son was getting the better of the argument, so she shifted her attack. "Why not become a merchant like the Browns in Providence?"

"I'd like to very much," replied Christopher, "but first of all I must get money and the only way I can do that is to sail somebody else's ship until I can buy one of my own. That's what the Browns did. They sailed for others and now they let other men do the sailing while they make even more money by staying home."

Mrs. Perry sighed. "I still think there are other ways to make money besides risking your life on the ocean, but then I can see that there is no use arguing with you."

Mrs. Perry was right. There was no sense in trying to argue a man into staying home after he had been to sea for ten years. Christopher Perry had shipped on a privateer when he was only fourteen years old. That was during the war with England and now that he was twenty-four he could look back on having spent three months on the British prison ship *Jersey* in New York Harbor, having served on the U.S. ship *Trumbull* in its 2½-hour engagement with the British letter of marque *Watt,* having spent eighteen months in an Irish prison after having been captured aboard a privateer, and following the war having served as mate of one merchantman and as captain of another. Keeping him on land would be like trying to keep an elephant in a hen house.

So Christopher Perry went to Newport the next day and before long he had signed on another merchantman, had packed his seaman's chest and had sailed for the East, leaving his wife to devote herself to their young son.

That was the way of it for several years. Christopher Perry would be gone sometimes as long as two years. Then he would return home for a few months before setting out on another voyage. He couldn't afford to stay home long, for trade was reviving, as he said it would. In 1787 John Brown's new 1,000-ton ship, the *General Washington,* cleared Providence for Canton with a cargo of anchors, cannon shot, iron, tar, rum, and wine. She was gone for two years, but when she returned, after having sailed 32,000 miles, she brought back a rich cargo. The first direct trade between Rhode Island and China had been established.

Trade was reviving but not so quickly as it might have, for in 1789, when George Washington was inaugurated, the Barbary pirates were still capturing American ships in the Mediterranean. On top of that, Spain refused the United States permission to navigate on the Mississippi River and England still had made no trade treaty with her former colonies. Men like Captain Perry talked of forming a navy to protect our shipping.

Then another son, Raymond, was born to Christopher Perry, and his wife began thinking about an education for their first child. She had read much to young Oliver Hazard Perry, but now that she also had Raymond to care for her time was limited. She turned to her father-in-law for advice.

"There's a school on Tower Hill, run by old Master Kelly," Judge Freeman Perry told her, "but I doubt if young Oliver is old enough to go there yet. Still, I can't think of another school in the whole South Country."

"But there are so many children around here of Oliver's age, it seems a shame that there is no place for them to be schooled."

"Some of us have been trying to get John Peckham to start a school. He's a well-educated man, but somewhat lazy and has never gotten around to it. Suppose I try him again?"

"That would be better than nothing."

Two days later Judge Perry brought home the news that John Peckham had agreed to start the school on one condition.

"What is that?" asked Oliver's mother and grandmother in unison.

"He wants to do his teaching lying down," explained the Judge.

"That's the silliest thing I ever heard of," snapped Grandmother Perry.

"It is a trifle odd," her husband said, "but that's the condition, and if you want a school for Oliver I suggest you make the best of it."

They did and the following Monday morning, Oliver Hazard Perry and two cousins, Sarah and Abby, from the adjacent farm of his uncle Dr. Joshua Perry, went to the home of John Peckham to start their education.

The classroom was the spare living room in Peckham's house. It had a low ceiling, small, narrow windows, and practically no furniture. There was not even a rug on the floor, so that the irregularities in the wide, pine floor boards were accentuated.

Peckham had lined up half a dozen straight-back chairs of various designs along one side of the fireplace and had placed his bed on the other side. When Oliver and his cousins entered the room, Peckham was lying on his bed and a boy about nine years old was sitting in a chair beside the bed.

The man looked over his octagonal glasses, grunted, and laid aside the paper he had been reading. One could easily see that he was more interested in reading about George Washington's recent visit to Providence and Newport than in taking charge of his class. He slowly rose to a sitting position and examined the trio which stood hesitantly on the threshold. Finally he spoke:

"Sit down in those chairs. There are three more pupils to come." Then as an afterthought, he said: "This is my nephew William. He is to be my assistant." With that he went back to his reading.

In a short while the other pupils arrived and Peckham began teaching. He had only two books for the six pupils, an alphabet for the younger ones and a primer for those who were beginning to read. Consequently, while one group recited, the other gathered in a corner and tried to study. The system did not work too well, for there was much squirming and giggling from the Perry children who were supposed to be studying.

Suddenly the teacher's voice cracked out.

"Oliver Perry, stand up!"

Young Perry stumbled to his feet.

"Hold your hands out, palms up!"

Perry obeyed, but to his astonishment the

teacher did not leave the bed. Rather he handed his ferrule to his nephew and ordered him to administer three sharp cracks to each hand.

Oliver clenched his teeth and vowed to himself that he would utter not a sound. No boy, no matter how much older, was going to make him cry. Down came the ferrule and with it a mighty sting, but Oliver just bit his lip harder. Again and again the ferrule fell with the force that only a bigger boy can apply to a smaller one, but not a murmur came from Perry.

"I won't cry. I won't cry," he kept repeating to himself; when the sixth blow had landed, he swallowed hard and drew a deep breath. "There," he said to himself, "you didn't make me cry."

But he might just as well have said the words out loud, for they were written on his face.

CHAPTER THREE

Old Master Kelly

SARAH WALLACE PERRY WASN'T GOING TO MAKE A mollycoddle out of her oldest son, nor was she going to allow him to be taught by a man who was too lazy to deal out his own punishment. With her husband at sea, she once again had to turn to her father-in-law.

"What shall I do?" she asked.

"Well, you want to remember that Peckham is only running this school because we asked him to," said Judge Perry, "and my advice would be to leave Oliver where he is until he can enter the Tower Hill School. Besides I should say he was doing quite well, what with the teaching you give him and his schooling by Peckham."

As usual the judge was right. Oliver was making good progress in his reading and writing, and for one whose ancestors had been peaceful Quakers, he also was getting to know something about war. His father, when he was home, had tales to tell about privateering in the Revolution; his mother told him stories about the suppression of the people in her homeland, Ireland; and his grandmother, not to be outdone, told of the Great Swamp Fight which had been held not five miles west of the Perry home and which ended Indian resistance in New England.

So Oliver continued to attend John Peckham's makeshift school until arrangements could be made for him to change.

Meanwhile his father came home again to learn that Benjamin Franklin had died; that Rhode Island had ratified the United States Constitution; that the meetinghouse on Tower Hill had burned; that a man named Slater had opened a cotton factory in Pawtucket; and that Arthur Fenner had been elected the first governor of Rhode Island.

Then one bright morning in October, 1792, Oliver and his two cousins started on their four-mile walk to Tower Hill where Old Master Kelly kept school in Squire Case's house.

They followed the post road toward Providence, down into a little valley, across a small stream and finally up Tower Hill. Once on the top of the hill they could look out across the West Passage of Narragansett Bay toward Conanicut Island. Farther south they could see Point Judith. Just ahead of them, to the north, was a crossroad which was the basis of a little settlement.

The houses in the village for the most part were large, gambrel-roofed affairs and the one nearest the crossroads had a large, wooden sign swinging in front of it.

"Pro Bono Publico," Oliver laboriously read aloud. "I wonder what that means?"

Neither of his cousins was able to answer, but all three mouthed the phrase as they continued along. At the crossroads they turned right, toward the bay.

As befitting the male member of the party Oliver observed:

"If you follow up the shore toward Providence you'll come to the South Ferry which takes you out to the island. Then you cross the island and take another ferry if you want to go to Newport."

His companions maintained a respectful silence, but their gazes were fixed on the last house on the right-hand side of the street, the Squire Case house.

Standing in the doorway was a stout, ruddy-faced old man. He was wearing a frock coat, ruffled shirt front, knickerbockers, long white stockings, and black shoes with silver buckles.

"That must be Master Kelly," said Sarah Perry.

The others nodded agreement, for now they were within earshot of their new teacher and he was watching them. As they approached the front door of the house, Master Kelly spoke.

"Ah, good morning."

The three Perrys returned his greeting.

"I take it this is Oliver Perry and his cousins, Sarah and Abby."

Again the three children answered in unison.

"Well, I am very pleased to see you. School would not seem like school unless I had a Perry in it. You see, I taught your fathers and your grandfather too. And, Master Perry," he added, herding the trio into the house ahead of him, "I might add that your grandfather was a much better student than your father."

CHAPTER FOUR

A Problem Solved

OLD MASTER KELLY'S DISTINCTION OF HAVING TAUGHT three generations of Perrys was somewhat hollow, for Oliver attended the Tower Hill School for only a few months before Kelly retired. It seemed almost as if he had just waited for Oliver to enroll.

"Oh, heavens!" said Mrs. Perry when she heard the news. "We'll never get you educated at this rate. Is anyone going to take Master Kelly's place?"

"He told us that a Mr. Southworth is coming from Connecticut."

Mrs. Perry sighed. "I wish your father were here," she said half to herself.

No sooner were the words out of her mouth than the front door opened and there stood Christopher Perry, complete in light-colored pantaloons and frock coat. There was no doubt that his voyage had been a successful one.

Oliver's face lighted up and he bounded to his father's side.

"What did you bring me from South America?" was his first question.

Christopher Perry put a hand on his son's shoulder and replied:

"Belay that. Time enough for presents when

they fetch my chest from the pier." He turned to his wife. "Surprised, are you?"

"Gracious, yes. I didn't expect you for another week."

"Well, we ran into a spell of weather off the Florida coast that would have had us here even sooner if it hadn't blown out to sea."

Oliver's father dropped into a chair by the fireplace and prepared to greet the other members of his family as well as his neighbors, to whom the word of his arrival was even now being passed. The rest of the afternoon he stayed in that chair, answering questions about South America, describing incidents of the voyage, and listening to the news of the countryside. As usual there was much to be said on all sides. The biggest piece of news to him was the fact that he now had a daughter, Sarah, as well as two sons. He knew that John Paul Jones had died, but he didn't know that Kentucky had been admitted to the United States, nor did he know about the successful trip of Elijah Ormsbee's steamboat on the Providence River.

Even after dinner when only the family remained he continued to talk and it was not until nine o'clock that his wife was able to bring up the subject of Oliver's education.

"Well," Oliver's father said. "I'd let him stay where he is. No use worrying about a man overboard until you hear him hit the water. If this Southworth turns out to be no good, we can start thinking then what to do about Oliver. Besides, I have half a mind to move to Newport. The family is getting too big for this house and I'd be nearer my business."

"I'd hate to see you leave South Kingstown," his father spoke up. "Why don't you build a house here? You aren't going to be sailing all your life."

"No," replied Christopher Perry, "I'm not going to be sailing all my life. When I get enough money tucked away I'm going to retire."

"Why not retire in South Kingstown?" asked his father. "Tell you what I'll do. I'll give you that ten-acre lot that joins the one I gave Joshua. You could build a house on it now, so your family could have more room, and then you could come back to it when you retired."

"I'm much obliged to you," said Christopher, "and I'll take the lot, if you are anxious to get rid of it, but I'll wait a while longer before building a house. I'm not just sure that I want to retire in South Kingstown."

"You may have the lot," said his father. "Perhaps it will help you to decide to settle here."

So it was left, and two months later Oliver's father was off on another voyage, this time to Europe. Meanwhile Oliver continued to attend the Tower Hill School.

But the arrangement didn't last. The following year, 1793, Oliver's uncle, Dr. Joshua Perry, took charge of the educational program. He came through the fields one evening and presented a new plan.

"I think I have solved the problem," he announced.

"How?" asked Oliver's mother, to whom the

business of educating Oliver, age eight; Raymond, age four; and Sarah, age two, was becoming more than just a problem.

"By hiring a tutor," replied Dr. Perry. "One of my patients told me today of a Scotsman by the name of Bryer, who is looking for a position. It seems that he recently served as tutor in Governor Fenner's family."

"And why did he leave the governor's family?" asked Mrs. Perry with a woman's canniness.

"I didn't think to ask," replied the doctor, "but it seems to me that if this Bryer was good enough for the governor, he should be good enough for us."

Eventually Dr. Perry had his way and Mr. Bryer moved into the doctor's house and set up a tutoring school, but it was not long before it was discovered why Mr. Bryer no longer tutored the governor's children. He had a habit of taking protracted, sudden, and spasmodic vacations and when he returned his disposition rarely was any better than his breath.

Again there was an educational problem in the Perry family, but for once Oliver's father arrived home in time to handle it. He did so with dispatch. No sooner had he heard the details of the situation than he said:

"That settles it. We'll move to Newport. In fact, I shall go there myself tomorrow and inquire into the purchase of a house."

CHAPTER FIVE

Newport

NEWPORT WAS AS DIFFERENT FROM SOUTH KINGSTOWN as black is from white. Stagecoaches ran daily to Boston from Newport; once a week from South Kingstown. Oliver was impressed, too, by the way houses were built flush to the streets and side by side.

He noticed a difference in the inhabitants, although that was not so surprising when one considered the fact that the farmers and the townsfolk never agreed in Rhode Island anyway.

Newporters thought in terms of ships and cargoes and the South Country people thought in terms of land and crops. That was one reason why Oliver liked Newport. He preferred ships and cargoes to land and crops, just like his father.

Along the water front on Thames Street one could watch the sloops and schooners in which the coasting trade was carried on and the square-riggers that had more ambitious destinations. There were ships enough to satisfy anyone, for Newport was even more of a seaport than Providence or New York. It was easier for ships to make Newport Harbor in the prevailing westerlies and there was less likelihood of a freeze-up in winter.

The ships left their mark on the city too. Ship-owners had their own stores in which they sold their cargoes. A person could get about anything he wanted in those shops. Shipyards, ropewalks, sail lofts, and sailors were as much a part of Newport as the ships themselves. So, too, the smells of tar and fish and the long boats shuttling between deep-water vessels and the wharves.

KETCH

Newport had something else that South Kingstown lacked, something abstract, yet remarkably noticeable. South Kingstown had always been a peaceful, self-sufficient country, whereas Newport had always been a bustling community, having much intercourse with the outside world, lots of commerce and its ensuing competition, and consequently, a stormy history.

Because of its excellent harbor Newport had

been a seaport from its beginning. First it had shipped dairy products from Rhode Island to the West Indies, then it became a slave-trade center, and in turn a base for privateers and a summer resort for wealthy Southerners. That was before the Revolution and the subsequent occupations by the British and French.

Now, in 1793, when Christopher Perry decided to move his family, Newport no longer was a city, but its trade was reviving. England and France were at war and American merchantmen were carrying supplies.

So the Perrys moved to Newport and Oliver was dispatched to the classical school kept by one John Fraser in New Church Lane.

"You want to be careful with old Fraser," a companion warned him the first day. "He gets mad awfully easy."

Oliver smiled his thanks. He'd been in enough schools to know what to expect in the way of discipline. Besides, he was anxious to learn.

"If you ever expect to be a captain," his father had told him time and again, "you'll have to know more than reading and writing. You'll have to know Latin and Spanish and mathematics."

And those were precisely the subjects that John Fraser taught and he taught them with a puritanical passion. It was not enough that a student had been through his Latin grammar once. Three times were not too many.

For two days Oliver attended school without incident, but on the third day he unwittingly aroused John Fraser's wrath. It happened during Latin recitation. The boy next to him leaned over and whispered, but Oliver did not hear what the boy had said, so turned his head and whispered, "What?"

No sooner had the word left his mouth than something whistled past his head and clattered against the wall behind him. Old Fraser had thrown a ferrule at him.

Oliver glared at his teacher and Fraser glared back.

"You have been here long enough, Master Perry, to know that whispering is not allowed in this school."

Oliver clenched his fists and stood up. He was so mad he couldn't speak. His jaw muscles flexed. He hesitated, wondering what to do. Finally, he snatched up his hat and marched out of the room— out of the room and out of the building.

All the way home he thought of things he might have said to old Fraser and what he would say to his mother.

"One thing," he muttered to himself, "I'm not going back to that school."

That was the first thing he told his mother as he stepped into the house. After that he explained what had happened.

His mother listened patiently. The teacher of course was wrong, but it was not for Oliver to decide whether he should return to school or not. If she let him have his own way in this instance, he would want his way again. Better not do anything today. Better wait until tomorrow.

The next morning when it was time for school, Mrs. Perry called Oliver.

"Here is a note I want you to deliver to Mr. Fraser. I do not think he will bother you any more."

Oliver looked at his mother a long time before answering.

"Are you ordering me to return to school?" he finally asked.

"Yes, Oliver," she replied. "You may consider it as an order."

Oliver took the note, placed his hat on his head, and marched stiffly up the street.

Much as he disliked the thought of having to study again under John Fraser, he disliked even more the thought of disobeying orders. Besides, John Fraser might have an ugly temper, but he also taught mathematics, the chief tool of navigators. So Oliver decided to pay strict attention to his studies and ignore John Fraser as much as possible.

The system worked well, for the more he concentrated on his studies the more he progressed and the more John Fraser came to like him.

Being liked was one of Oliver's chief stocks in trade. It was not only those of his own age with whom he was popular, but older people as well. He seemed older than most of the boys of his age. He had read more and he had associated with older people more. That was because his father was away so much, leaving Oliver as the man of the house.

Oliver enjoyed the role. He sat at the head of the table during dinner and lavished conversation on his mother. The practice served in good stead, for Newport was leaning toward formal dinners these days and it was not long before invitations were being offered to Oliver as well as Mrs. Perry. Count de Rochambeau, son of the French general, was one who had a particular fondness for Oliver. He invited him to dinner often and gave him the run of his large library.

John Fraser, strangely enough, was another who enjoyed the lad's company. He invited Oliver to attend his nightly classes in navigation and often in spare moments would take him to the beach in order to give him practice in the use of the sextant.

Most Newport boys of Oliver's age were supposed to be seen, and not heard, but Oliver was seen, heard, and what is more important, listened to.

Fraser summed up the situation in one sentence when he said:

"Oliver is a better navigator right now than most of the captains in the city."

CHAPTER SIX

The New Navy

CAPTAIN CHRISTOPHER PERRY, BEING A MAN OF CONsiderable experience, seldom had difficulty in obtaining an audience whenever he put in an appearance along the Newport water front. Between voyages, his appearances along the water front were frequent; besides liking to talk shop, he also liked to keep his fingers on the affairs of the port. No telling when an opportunity for a smart captain was likely to turn up. If the weather was mild, Captain Perry usually could be found along the wharves or in the warehouses. If the weather was raw, he could be found in the tavern or some owner's office or store. And if school was not in session, Oliver could be found with him, always listening and learning.

"What this country needs, is a navy—a good navy," was one of Captain Perry's favorite themes. "Our commerce is reaching the point where it needs protection badly. I have no idea how much it amounts to in dollars and cents, but I do know that you rarely reach any foreign port without finding an American ship there ahead of you. And these foreigners know we have no way of protecting ourselves. Why, it's worth your life to enter the Mediterranean.

The Barbary pirates are making slaves out of American seamen. Pretty soon American captains are going to refuse to ship to those waters, and then where will our commerce go to?"

"There are other ports besides those in the Mediterranean," a friend might argue.

"Very true," Captain Perry would reply, "but there are other countries besides the Barbary States, which are not beyond pirating. If one country can get away with piracy against us, then the others will try it; and before you know it, there won't be any port safe for our ships. Why, even France is beginning to pick on us. She's got privateers just lying in wait for our ships down in the Caribbean. And England! She hasn't reached the point of piracy, but she's doing something just as bad—searching our ships for British sailors. That wouldn't be so bad if she took only British sailors, but she needs men so badly, she's taking American subjects!"

"But it costs money to build a navy," a conservative would object.

"We could have two navies for all the money we have given the Barbary pirates for tribute," Captain Perry would reply.

"European nations pay tribute to the Barbary pirates. It seems to be the best system."

"It is for them. The highest bidder gets the protection of the Barbary pirates and, hence, gets all the trade. The European nations can afford that sort of thing, but we can't. Our only choice is to lick the Barbary pirates once and for all."

That seemed to be the opinion of President George Washington too, for in 1794 he finally convinced Congress that the Algerian situation was getting serious. The United States would be ruined if American ships were not allowed to do business in the Mediterranean.

It was a great day for Captain Perry when he learned that Congress had voted to build six frigates of not less than 32 guns each, for he, among others, had been advocating the building of a navy for more than eight years. Captain Perry was equally pleased to learn shortly afterward that President Washington had chosen John Barry, Samuel Nicholson, Silas Talbot, Joshua Barney, Richard Dale, and Thomas

Truxton to oversee the building of the frigates. Barry, Talbot, Barney, and Truxton had all been privateer captains during the war with England, while Dale had served under John Paul Jones. Captain Perry was somewhat partial to privateersmen.

Talbot was assigned to the *Constitution,* 44 guns, at Boston; Nicholson was given charge of the *President,* 44 guns, at New York; Barry got the *United States,* 44 guns, at Philadelphia; Barney went to Portsmouth, Virginia, to supervise the building of the *Chesapeake,* 38 guns; Dale was given the *Constellation,* 38 guns, at Baltimore; and Truxton the *Congress,* 38 guns, at Portsmouth, New Hampshire.

The only catch to all this as far as Captain Perry could see was one clause in the act creating these ships, which stated that all work on the ships should stop if a peace was established with Algiers while the fleet was being built.

Oliver Hazard Perry's education was greatly expedited by just such clauses as this, for every time one was promulgated his father would expound for days at a time. During these periods, Captain Perry would cover the history of the subject thoroughly as well as the ancestry of the parties that perpetrated the measure. Oliver received considerable education this way during the year 1795, for the growing nation was making many mistakes.

For instance, Congress ratified a treaty with England and not one word was included about the impressment of American seamen. Captain Perry was not alone in blasting that treaty. Alexander

Hamilton was stoned and an effigy of John Jay was burned.

Then came the peace with Algiers. Oliver thought his father would burst a blood vessel.

"A million dollars, just like that," roared Captain Perry, snapping his fingers. "I don't mind the eight hundred thousand dollars to ransom the American seamen being held as slaves by the Dey of Algiers, but giving that old goat a hundred thousand dollar frigate is suicide. Here we haven't got a single ship we can call our own and yet we promise to give him a thirty-six-gun frigate, so he can turn around and use it against our merchantmen. On top of that we have to pay him twenty-three thousand dollars a year to keep him quiet.

"I'd like to know what Congress uses for brains. Stop building the six frigates, says Congress, because the Dey of Algiers has promised to be a good boy. What does Congress know about the Dey of Algiers? Has Congress ever seen an Algerian pirate? Certainly not, yet it is willing to trust one four thousand miles away. You wait and see, not only Algiers, but every other country on the Barbary Coast will pick on us more than ever."

Oliver's family was not sure, but his mother for one felt that Captain Perry's rantings and ravings had some effect on Congress.

"Your father's arguments are sound," she told Oliver with a twinkle in her eye, "and I'm sure he must have been heard in Philadelphia."

Indeed, it would seem that he had been heard by Congress, for early in 1796, an act was passed calling for the completion of three of the six frigates under construction, the *Constitution*, the *United States*, and the *Constellation*.

Yet it was more than a year later that the *United States* slid down the ways of Philadelphia. It took four months more for blocks to be knocked from under the *Constellation* at Baltimore and still another month for the *Constitution* to feel Boston Harbor under her keel. These facts, heartening as they might be to seafaring Americans, had little if any effect on Europe, for French privateers continued to waylay American merchantmen in the Caribbean and English ships-of-war continued to impress American seamen.

CORSAIR

CHAPTER SEVEN

Westerly

FOR A LONG TIME CHRISTOPHER PERRY HAD LOOKED forward to the day when he could retire from the sea and settle down in some peaceful community and enjoy life. But why he picked the close of the year 1797 to do it, even his wife couldn't understand. Nor could she understand why he should want to leave Newport and the sea to live in Westerly.

"I'm worried about that siege of yellow fever in Providence," he gave as one excuse. "In two months it has killed thirty-six people and I'm afraid someone will bring it to Newport. We'd be safer in some out-of-the-way place like Westerly."

"But what about the trouble with France?" asked his wife. "Are you going to run away from that?"

"There'll be no trouble with France," Christopher Perry replied. "If the government hasn't courage enough to refuse to fight Algiers it won't have courage enough to fight France. Besides, as long as the French interfere with our trade, merchants are not going to risk their ships, and that means no work for me. I've saved up enough money to live comfortably and I might just as well live in Westerly where my money will go farther."

"But what about Oliver? He's nearly ready to take up a career."

"If I know Oliver, he'll be wanting to go to sea and this is no time for him to be doing that. He might just as well bide his time in Westerly as Newport."

"Christopher, I think you are just mad with the government for being so slow about building a navy."

"Well, why shouldn't I be? One merchant crew spent five years in slavery because Congress wouldn't build a navy and fight the Dey of Algiers."

At this point Christopher Perry began thumping his fist on the table and bellowing at his wife.

"Hush, hush!" she said. "Don't get so excited. It's all over now."

"It's not all over!" thundered Christopher Perry. "I wouldn't trust that Dey of Algiers as far as I could throw a capstan. As soon as he sees what the French are doing to our shipping, he'll start in again. Why should I, or Oliver, go to sea knowing that we had no navy behind us?"

"We have three frigates now."

"It would take more than three frigates to beat the French or the Algerians either, and by the time Congress got around to building any more, the first three probably would be captured. No, I'm going to retire and let somebody else worry about the navy."

And he did. As soon as he could clean up his affairs in Newport he moved his family to Westerly, where he bought a house on the Pawcatuck River.

His family, incidentally, now included three sons, Oliver, Raymond and Matthew, and two daughters, Sarah and Ann.

Westerly was just a stop on the post road to New York, a village of less than fifteen houses scattered along the river. Like South Kingstown, the inhabitants made their living from their farms. But being a sailor, Christopher Perry had always dreamed of a farm in just such an isolated spot.

And, sailor-like, he no sooner had got rid of his sea legs than he began to miss the ocean. Another reason that his retirement could not be termed successful was the fact that he continued to subscribe to the Newport *Mercury*. Once a week he and Oliver would go down to the crossroads to get his copy of the paper. The news in it usually was some three weeks old, but this, supplemented by the rumors that they picked up in the tavern, which served as post office and stage center, kept them fairly well acquainted with what was going on in the world. It also kept Christopher Perry discontented.

He had moved to Westerly in December and in January, 1798, he was beginning to grumble. Oliver felt the first tremors.

"Hmph," his father muttered as he looked up from his paper to watch for ruts in the road. "It looks like Congress may finally get around to doing something for American seamen. It says here that the House of Representatives has appointed a committee to bring in a bill for the relief and protection of American seamen. And here's something else

—a report in favor of arming American vessels. Ah, but there is a catch to it. Consideration of the report was postponed until the first Monday in February in order to allow time for receipt of information from France. Bah! While they're waiting another dozen ships will be captured!"

The next week Christopher Perry became a little madder.

"The American seamen's relief and protection bill was read twice in the House of Representatives," he read aloud from the *Mercury*. "Now, isn't that nice? Are we paying Congress to learn to read or to pass laws?"

It was like that all winter long. Christopher Perry would read the *Mercury*, get mad, and then spend the rest of the week cooling off. Then the process would be repeated. February was the worst month.

"Look at this!" he bellowed when the January 30th issue of the paper reached him. "An American merchant ship captured by the British frigate *Thetis!*"

He no sooner had seated himself to read further then he burst out again: "An undoubted authority says that the French have twenty-four ships-of-the-line building!"

Worse and worse the news became. A report from Savannah said that French ships had been ordered to take all American vessels. One captain said he had seen seventeen American ships held by the French at Nantes. In March came the report that sixty French privateers were fitting out at

Nantes and the same month the American envoys to Paris reported to President Adams of the United States that they had no hopes of even being officially received by the French government.

Winter moved toward spring and still Congress just talked. An appropriation for the fitting and arming of the three frigates was passed, but the discussion continued about the arming of merchant ships and the advisability of establishing an officer to handle the naval affairs of the country.

The committee that was behind the seamen's relief bill kept hammering away at Congress and finally in April the President was authorized to build or purchase twelve more ships.

That was more to Christopher Perry's liking and when on the last day of April a separate department for naval affairs was established, his enthusiasm boiled over.

"I'm going back to work," he suddenly announced. "If the government is going to build a fleet, it's going to need men to sail it. This is no time for able-bodied men to sit back and do nothing."

"You mean," replied his wife, with a twinkle in her eye, "that if the government is really going to war with France, you're not going to miss any of the excitement. You can't fool me. Ever since this trouble started you've been wondering how you could get into it."

Perry eyed his wife for a moment. The woman always took the wrong time to tease him. "You must admit," he finally said, "that experienced captains will be in demand."

"Of course," his wife replied with a smile, "and if you want to command one of those new ships you had better do something about it."

"I am. I shall write Secretary of War Pickering at once and volunteer my services." Perry paused for a moment. "I might volunteer a little advice too," he finally added.

"And what might that be?" asked his wife.

"I might tell John Adams to pick a sailor to run the new naval department."

CHAPTER EIGHT

The Man of the House

IT WAS THE MIDDLE OF JUNE, 1798, WHEN CHRIStopher Perry was notified that he was to be appointed a post captain in the navy. The letter was sent by Secretary of War Pickering, for, although Benjamin Stoddert of Virginia had been appointed Secretary of the Navy the previous month, he had not as yet taken office.

There was great excitement in the Perry household that night. Little Ann Maria, who was only seven months old, and her brother Matthew, three years old, did not know what it was all about, but seven-year-old Sarah and nine-year-old Raymond knew. And Oliver even went so far as to ask his father if he might go to sea with him.

Christopher Perry smiled at his son. "You're a little too young yet," he said. "Besides, I do not know when I shall sail. The government is looking for a ship for me and if it doesn't find one suitable, I shall have to wait for one to be built."

"If the government did that, you could have just the kind of ship you wanted," said Oliver.

"Yes, but I'd have to wait most a year before I could use it."

Toward the end of the month Christopher

Perry received another letter, this time from George Champlin of Newport. The government was considering the purchase of a ship being built at Warren, and Champlin had been asked to inspect the ship to see if it was suitable. He also had been asked to write Captain Perry suggesting that he, too, look at the ship.

"I'll go to Warren tomorrow," was the captain's reaction.

Three days later he was home again with the news that the government would take the ship.

"Mr. Champlin has approved her," he told his wife, "and that means the government will take her."

"It seems to me that it is more important that you approve of her," said Mrs. Perry.

"Well, I do," said the captain. "Cromwell and Child are good builders and Gibbs and Channing were smart enough to have her designed as much like the rest of the government ships as possible. Besides, by buying a ship already on the stocks, we'll save that much time."

"Where do Gibbs and Channing come in on it?"

"Well, they either had started to build her for themselves or, what is more likely, started the building after it was announced that the government was going to buy some more ships."

"What is she like?" asked Oliver.

"There is not much to see yet, but the plans call for her to be a hundred twenty-four feet long with a thirty-four-foot beam. She'll have two decks, three masts, and will carry twenty-four twelve-pounders on her main deck and six six-pounders on her forecastle and quarter-deck."

"What's to be her name?"

"That hasn't been decided yet, but I think I shall suggest *General Greene*. He is a Rhode Island hero and at the same time he was one of our ancestors."

"I suppose you will spend most of your time in Warren now," said Mrs. Perry.

"Yes, I am to supervise the building of the ship. In fact, I was thinking of moving the family to Warren."

"That would be rather expensive for such a short time."

"Well, then perhaps you and I and Ann Maria could move there and leave the rest of the children here."

"But who would look after them?"

"Oh, the Taylors and the Perrys and—why, Oliver could take charge." Captain Perry turned to his son. "How would you like that?"

Oliver decided quickly that he wouldn't like it. He would much prefer to go to Warren with his father, but he did not think it wise to say so. "Why," he finally answered, "I should be glad to take charge of the family here, if you didn't think I could be of use to you."

Captain Perry smiled. "I'm afraid you would be of more use here. Perhaps later we could send for you."

So that was the way it was left. Captain and

Mrs. Perry took Ann Maria to Warren, and Oliver stayed in Westerly with Matthew, Sarah, and Raymond.

There was not as much for Oliver to do as might be expected. The Negro housekeeper took care of running the house and all he had to do was act as the supreme authority for the other children. That was not difficult either, for they always had looked up to him. There was no school for him to attend and so he spent most of his time reading or sailing on the river and Little Narragansett Bay. Reading received the most attention, for he had always liked it. Besides, sailing rafts and skiffs wasn't much fun when you knew that your father was building a warship not more than thirty miles away.

Oliver brooded over that ship. It didn't seem right that he should not have some part in the plans for her. Boys younger than he had sailed on warships. The more he thought about the ship the more he wanted to go to Warren.

Throughout the summer Oliver mulled his problem, but no matter how he approached it, he always reached the same conclusion—he would have to persuade his father that he was old enough to go to sea.

Meanwhile the government was beginning to clear its decks. The treaty with France, which had been signed during the American Revolution, was revoked. Two days later authorization for the capture of armed French vessels was obtained, and on July 11, 1798, a marine corps was established. Then Congress ordered three more frigates to be built.

The summer dragged on for Oliver. While he played nursemaid in Westerly, naval activity was gathering steerageway. The *Delaware,* under Captain Decatur, captured the first French ship, the schooner *Le Croyable,* in June. The frigate *United States,* Captain Barry, took a 10-gun French privateer, *Sans Pareil,* in August, and an 8-gun sloop, the *Jaloux,* in September.

But the thing that set the country talking most was the capture of the French frigate *L'Insurgente* in February, 1799, by the United States frigate *Constellation,* under Captain Truxton. There was more to the story than just the taking of one of the fastest frigates on the seas. After Lieutenant John Rodgers, Midshipman David Porter, and eleven men had been put aboard the prize, a storm came up and for three days those thirteen men stood guard over 173 prisoners and at the same time managed the ship.

When the news reached Westerly, Oliver couldn't contain himself any longer. He wrote a letter to his father.

"I want to join the navy," he stated, "and I want to go to sea with you."

It seemed to Oliver that the war would be over before his father replied and when the letter did come it contained no definite answer.

"Write me your reasons," the letter said, "and if they are good enough I shall consider having you appointed a midshipman."

Oliver labored over that letter. He weighed every reason that came to his head and worded and reworded it. His best argument was the fact that his father had been but fourteen years old in 1775 when he joined the Kingston Reds to fight the British. Eventually Oliver posted his reply and then began another long wait.

It was a blustery, cold day in March when the answer came, the kind of day that would make even an experienced seaman think twice before leaving port. But Oliver wasn't thinking about such things this day, he was only interested in breaking the seal on the folded message from his father. He tore the paper, he was so eager. Then he had it open and was reading:

"I have recommended your appointment to the Secretary of the Navy. Your warrant should be here in a few weeks. . . ."

Then another wait, but this one did not seem so long, for there was much to be done. The *General Greene* had been launched in January and was now in Newport being rigged and fitted out. Mrs. Perry was ready to come home, for she had things to do too. She was going to move to Tower Hill so as to be near relatives while her menfolks were at sea. So while he was waiting for his warrant, Oliver helped his mother prepare to move.

Finally word came from his father that the warrant had arrived.

Two days later Oliver left for Newport.

"Remember," his mother told him as he said good-bye. "It is not your father you are sailing under, but Captain Perry of the United States Navy."

CHAPTER NINE

The "General Greene"

WHEN HE ARRIVED IN NEWPORT, OLIVER WENT directly to Thames Street where Gibbs and Channing, the navy's Newport agents, had their office. His father would be either there or on the ship which would be tied up near by.

As he walked down through Washington Square toward the water front, Oliver looked for the *General Greene*. It would be the only deep-water vessel at the wharves. Then he saw her or rather the yellow masts which seemed to have grown out of the gray shingled buildings on the wharves. He was tempted to go directly to the ship, but checked the impulse and instead entered the office. There was his father talking with an elderly gentleman in the rear of the building.

The two men did not see Oliver at first and he patiently stood to one side waiting for them to finish their conversation. Finally the older man looked up over his glasses at Oliver. At the same time Captain Perry turned and saw his son. Oliver snapped to attention, saluted and said:

"Midshipman Perry reporting, sir."

Captain Perry looked his son up and down before answering.

"Are you sure you are a midshipman?"

"Well, sir, you have my warrant."

"Have you signed your oath and returned it to the Secretary of Navy?"

"Well—no, sir."

"Then I am afraid you are not a midshipman yet. Would you say so, Mr. Gibbs?"

The older man smiled. "No," he said, "but I think he has the makings of one."

"But he hasn't even got a uniform," Captain Perry continued.

"But," said Oliver, "Mother thought we could get one easier in Newport."

"We?—and I didn't hear a 'sir' in that last sentence."

"I'm sorry, sir. Mother thought you could get me a uniform here in Newport."

"I get you a uniform? Since when was a captain supposed to—" Captain Perry could not keep the pretense up any longer, and both he and Mr. Gibbs broke out with chuckles. "All right, son, I guess Mr. Gibbs can get you a uniform all right, but remember, once you get it, I shall be Captain Perry to you and you will be Mr. Perry to me. Now, how would you like to see the ship?"

"I should like to very much, sir."

"Come along then."

They stepped out into Thames Street and headed for the company wharf only a few steps from the office. When the ship came into view suddenly from behind a building, Oliver stopped short. His eyes widened as though they were trying to swallow up the whole ship at once. Captain Perry had stopped too and was watching his son.

"What do you think of her?" he asked.

"She's a beauty," Oliver replied. "I didn't realize she was so big."

Captain Perry chuckled. "She won't seem so big when we try to jam 220 men onto her. Come aboard. I'll show you what I mean."

Up the gangplank they went, through an opening in the bulwarks and onto the spar deck. Captain Perry stopped and looked around. "There is a lot you have to learn about this ship," he said, "and you might just as well start now."

"Yes, sir."

"In the first place, the starboard gangway is reserved for officers. You must remember these little things because they make for good discipline and discipline often will determine the outcome of a battle."

Then Captain Perry began showing Midshipman Perry about the spar deck. First they went forward to the fo'c'sle where the captain pointed out the little platforms extending out over the water from which the lead was thrown for sounding bottom and from which the speed of the ship was logged.

"Channels or chains is what we call them. And here are your capstans for snugging anchors and hawsers. Your best seamen are stationed here. Sheet-anchor men, we call them. And I might say right here that if I were you I would make friends with some of these sheet-anchor men. They can teach you as much about sailing a ship as I can and probably more."

From the fo'c'sle they returned to midships. "This is the waist. The landlubbers among the crew are stationed here. They handle the simpler operations like tending sheets and braces. Waisters is the name for them."

On the quarter-deck Captain Perry pointed out the portholes in front of which 6-pound guns would be placed. He also explained how the starboard side of the quarter-deck was reserved for the captain, except on a port tack when the captain's domain was shifted to the weather, or higher, side of the quarter-deck.

"Any questions before we go below?"

"Yes, sir. Why are these walls so high?"

"Walls? Oh, you mean bulwarks. They protect the men on the spar deck in battle. They also help in a rough sea and as shields for the guns. Anything else?"

"Yes, sir. How am I going to learn the names of all these ropes and sails?"

"That's up to you. It will take some time, but it's part of your job. However, I can give you a good tip. Learn the workings of one mast and you have them all. In other words, the three masts are named fore, main, and mizzen. Each has much the same sails and sheets. For instance, the fore royal would naturally be on the foremast and the main royal on the mainmast. The same is true of topgallant sails and topsails."

Oliver's brow was beginning to pucker.

"Enough," Captain Perry said. "No sense getting you all confused now. It will all come gradually. Now let's go below. This afterhatch here is reserved for officers. The crew uses the hatch leading down from the fo'c'sle."

When they reached the gun deck, Captain Perry had to remove his hat and even stoop a little to avoid striking his head. "Five feet ten inches is all the government allows above this main deck. Most of the crew will eat and sleep here. The galley is forward of the mainmast and the crew's hammocks will be swung there. In order of rank come the warrant officers, midshipmen, and lieutenants until you reach the stern of the ship where my cabins are located."

Captain Perry then went on to explain how during the day the ship's carpenter, cooper, barber, and cobbler would set up their shops between the 12-pound guns which would line both sides of the deck.

"I might even set up a classroom for the midshipmen," Captain Perry added.

"Classroom?"

"Yes. There will be seven of you reefers and if you ever expect to become officers you will have to know more than how to handle sails. Now come aft and see my cabins."

Stepping through a door in a partition across the deck, Captain Perry stopped.

"This is my dining room, but it won't be used for that purpose very often. The sailing master will use the big table there for charting his courses and then should we get into battle the partition will come down, the furniture be moved out, and four guns operated through the ports you see."

Then Captain Perry stepped into the next room. The one they had just left was small enough, about 20 feet wide and 12 feet long, but this one was even smaller. It did have more light, however, being benefited by two large portholes in the stern of the ship. To port and starboard of the captain's cabin were doors. Oliver looked at his father inquiringly.

"Sleeping rooms. If I should ever be visited by the commodore of the fleet I'd have to move into one of the sleeping rooms and let him have the other. He'd also take over my main cabin here and the dining room as well."

After the inspection of the cabin was over, Captain Perry took Oliver into the hold, which was divided up into storerooms, magazines, lockers for the craftsmen, and a few sleeping rooms. Then they went up onto the spar deck again.

"There," said Captain Perry as they reached daylight. "How do you think you'll like your new home?"

"'I shall like it, sir. Better, perhaps, after I have learned to sleep in a hammock."

Captain Perry laughed. "Well, maybe someday you won't have to sleep in a hammock. Maybe you'll have a cabin like mine." Oliver's father started to lead the way to the gangplank and then suddenly stopped. "There is one more thing I want to tell you. In the navy, it's 'Aye, sir,' not 'Yes, sir.' If you are called, you reply 'Aye, sir'; if you are given an order you reply, 'Aye, aye, sir.' "

Oliver looked up into his father's eyes and found a twinkle there.

"Aye, aye, sir," he replied.

SAILORS' MESS

CHAPTER TEN

Trouble in Port

ALL THAT REMAINED TO BE DONE TO THE *General Greene* was to take her out into deeper water and ship supplies and guns, but Captain Perry did not want to do that until he had a full crew—and seamen were scarce in Newport.

The delay was not improving the captain's disposition.

"Imagine it," he would fume, "having to bribe men to go to sea. What's this world coming to, anyway? No one had to force me to enlist in the Revolution."

"Times have changed," someone might argue.

"Bosh!" Perry would reply. "You mean men have changed. They'd rather go without nowadays than take a little risk and earn some prize money. Four thousand dollars I've spent for recruiting and what have I got? Fifty seamen and not very good ones at that. Of course I haven't heard from the stations I set up in Boston and Salem and New London, but imagine having to go that far for men!"

Oliver was anxious to get to sea, too. He had his uniform now and even his father admitted he looked well in it. The coat was a plain blue frock, lined and edged with buff. It had no lapels like his father's, but it had a standing collar of buff and plain buff cuffs. His vest was plain and buff and his muscle-revealing breeches buff too.

But while Captain Perry had to attend to the business of signing on a crew, Oliver could spend much of his time ashore, showing off his uniform to his friends in Newport. His only complaint was that he was not allowed to wear his small, yellow, mounted sword ashore.

April turned to May and still the *General Greene* lacked a full crew. Thirty blue and red dressed marines had arrived and Captain Perry had been given $2,000 more for recruiting purposes, but it still did not look as if the *General Greene* would sail for Havana on May 15th, as the Secretary of Navy had ordered.

That date came and went and with it several terse letters from the secretary to Captain Perry.

"Blast him," the captain would mutter. "He sits down there in Philadelphia and sees no reason why I shouldn't sail. Let him come up here and try to sign on a crew. You'd think all I had to do was pick out my men and order them aboard. It's not only the fact that there are no men available, but those we do sign are liable to leave before the rest of the crew can be gotten. But I'll get sailors if I have to pay a thousand dollars apiece for them."

He already had spent $6,000 for recruiting rendezvous and advances in pay. Within a week he obtained $2,500 more from Gibbs and Channing. That was May 23rd. Two days later, armed with another $600, he rounded up the last of his crew.

But that wasn't the end of Captain Perry's troubles. First of all the guns had to be shipped. Then came provisions and water. Barrel after barrel was put aboard, for the *General Greene* was to provision two other ships when she got to Havana. All this took four days.

Finally, Captain Perry was ready to put to sea. He made one more visit to the office of Gibbs and Channing and there received another letter from the Secretary of Navy.

"Humph," he muttered as he read. "Still telling me how to run my ship." Then he turned to Mr. Gibbs and held out his hand. "We break ground in the morning."

Mr. Gibbs took the captain's hand.

"Good luck and I hope you capture many a French prize."

With that Captain Perry marched out of the office and down to the wharf where his gig awaited him. He stepped into the stern sheets and the oarsmen pushed off.

When the officer of the watch ordered all hands called at four bells the next morning, there was a fair southwest wind rippling the harbor. The sun was climbing up from behind the town as the boatswain's whistle sounded. Presently the signal was repeated and the voice of the boatswain's mates came up from the gun deck: "Up all idlers" . . . "Heave out and lash up" . . . "Rouse and shine."

There was the sound of feet thumping on the deck and presently sleepy-eyed sailors began pouring out of the hatches, each carrying his hammock.

Several of the crew climbed on top of the bulwarks and began stowing hammocks as they were passed up. In twelve minutes the work was done and the seamen turned to cleaning the decks. They rolled up their bell-bottomed trousers and after water had been pumped up from the harbor, began dragging holystones back and forth across the deck.

LASHING AND STOWING HAMMOCKS

Meanwhile the cooks had started breakfast and by the time the gunners' mates had shined their guns and the seamen had squeegeed the decks it was seven o'clock and the crew was piped to breakfast.

Down in his hammock on the gun deck with the rest of the officers, Oliver had heard all this going on. He had heard it every morning since the ship was finished, but somehow this morning he wanted to get up even if there was nothing for him to do. Every day he had been in Newport had been the same. All he had done was stand around and watch. First it was the men putting the finishing touches on the ship. Then it was the loading of the piles of slate for ballast. Finally it was the provisioning.

The provisioning had taken a long while. Oliver had had to stand around and watch while barrel after barrel was swung aboard. Nearly 5,000 gallons of rum had been obtained for the twice daily ration of grog, 950 gallons of vinegar for disinfecting purposes in battle, 170 barrels of beef, 170 barrels of port, and more of rice, butter, cheese, soup, flour, meal, bread, oil, potatoes, and salt fish. And all Oliver had done was run a few errands for his father.

Today was different. The slap of the water against the ship had a different sound. The seamen above seemd to push their holystones with more vigor. The boatswain's whistle was a little shriller. Today was the day the *General Greene* would break ground.

Oliver didn't have to be called. He was already dressing when six strokes were sounded on the ship's bell. The other six midshipmen tumbled from their hammocks.

"What are you doing up so early?" one of them asked Oliver. "You don't have to make a good impression on the captain."

Oliver smiled. "Don't worry. I shall probably wish he wasn't my father before this cruise is up. He'll probably treat me a lot worse than the rest of you, just so there'll be no hard feelings."

If the rest of the midshipmen had thought that Oliver was going to be hard to get along with, they were quickly learning otherwise. Oliver had a way with him.

The seven boys sat down to breakfast as though they were in boarding school and scarcely paid any attention to their food, except to notice that each got his share.

Breakfast didn't go quickly enough for Oliver and it seemed even longer before eight bells sounded and the colors run up. Then he learned that he had to put in his usual two hours of study that morning. He wanted to rebel, but quickly thought better of it.

Most of the crew were going about their usual tasks and so must he. The carpenters, cooper, armorer, and sailmaker all set up their shops and started work. Others, however, were finishing up preparations for putting to sea.

One thing Oliver had accomplished in the time he had been aboard ship was to strike up an acquaintance with one of the sheet-anchormen, a weathered old fellow by the name of Joseph Weaver, who had sailed with John Paul Jones on the *Bon Homme Richard*. Oliver also had discovered that he could get more information out of Weaver than he could get out of his father. In the first place, Oliver could make Weaver stop his work whenever he wanted to, whereas he had to wait if he wanted to speak with his father. Even then he received only terse answers. Weaver was much different. He liked to talk with Oliver. It was much easier to use the tongue than the hands.

So this day, when he had the chance, Oliver took his troubles forward.

"Weaver."

"Aye, sir."

"I want to talk to you a moment."

"Aye, aye, sir."

Weaver dropped the rope he was coiling.

"Weaver, what's all this business of scrubbing got to do with getting under way?"

"Well, sir, it looks like the captain isn't quite ready yet and he just wants to keep the men busy."

"Do you think we'll leave today?"

"Begging your pardon, sir, but I don't think we'll leave unless we do it pretty quick."

"What do you mean?"

"Well, sir, it's none of my business, but this breeze is going to fade out pretty soon, or I don't know Newport Harbor."

"I see." Oliver hesitated a moment and then, being unable to think of any more questions, said, "That is all, Weaver. Thank you."

"Aye, aye, sir."

Toward noon, however, the order finally came.

"All hands to make sail."

There was a scurrying of feet. The capstan was manned, the topsails loosed and the anchor broken out, but while Lieutenant Laing could order the sails loosed, he could do nothing about filling them. If a topsail filled, a jib would slat, and pretty soon they all were slatting.

"We'll never clear Goat Island at this rate," Oliver heard his father say to Lieutenant Laing. "Better let go the anchor."

And that was as far as the *General Greene* got that day and the next.

On May 30th, and the day after, the wind was from the west. Then when it finally did swing, it came from northeast and blew a gale. Captain Perry tried to get under way on June 1st, but quickly clewed up his sails for fear of losing them. Finally, on June 2nd, the wooden image of *General Greene* pointed out past Goat Island and into the East Passage of Narragansett Bay.

CHAPTER ELEVEN

First Voyage

OLIVER HAD HAD SOME TASTE OF SHIP ROUTINE WHILE the *General Greene* had been in Newport harbor, but once at sea he soon learned that being a sailor was more work than fun. No allowance was made for his age or that of any of the other young midshipmen. They had their watches to stand like any other member of the crew and chances to sleep were few. Four hours on deck and four hours off were the regular orders; if the wind kicked up, the whole crew was held ready to reef, douse or trim sail. And the wind did kick up, not more than thirty-six hours out of Newport, somewhere off Sandy Hook.

The starboard watch, to which Oliver had been assigned, had just relieved the port watch at midnight when the wind began to freshen. Lieutenant Jeremiah Fenner, officer of the watch, eyed his compass and then squinted aloft at his sails.

"Mr. Perry," he barked.

Oliver jumped from the lee of the hatch where he had been sitting, lifted his cap and replied:

"Aye, sir?"

"Tell Captain Perry the wind is swinging and freshening and that it looks as if we might be running into a storm."

"Aye, aye, sir."

Oliver scrambled down the hatch to his father's cabin, knocked, and was admitted. He delivered the message and waited for an answer.

"Tell Mr. Fenner to hold his course and that I shall be coming up immediately."

"Aye, aye, sir."

Oliver returned on deck and was followed shortly afterward by his father. The officers raised their caps as the captain appeared. Then he, too, eyed both compass and sails.

"I've a mind to test this ship," he said to Lieutenant Fenner. "We're still in familiar waters and we might just as well learn now what she'll do. You may turn up all hands. I'll have two reefs in those topsails, if you please, and you may clew up your staysails."

"Aye, aye, sir."

Quickly came the roll of a drum, followed by the pipings of the boatswain and his mates. The port watch came grumbling from the forward hatches. Then came more pipings as orders to reef and douse the sails were given. The topmast hands inched out on the footropes and began tying in their reefs.

The wind already had begun to howl out of the north and with it came a driving rain. The sea picked up and the *General Greene* began dipping and climbing with the swells. Oliver moved to the southern side of the afterhatch to get as much protection as possible and still be available for any orders.

There was not much for him to do, but there was plenty for the seamen. Captain Perry ordered the topgallant masts sent down and the log heaved every glass. It was important that he know exactly how fast the ship was traveling.

"Six knots," came the report from the chains and Lieutenant Fenner marked the new speed down on the traverse board.

Then Captain Perry ordered all guns double-lashed.

The two master's mates at the helm were having their hands full in trying to keep the *General Greene* from broaching to. The following seas tested them constantly and they had to saw back and forth on the wheel after each swell to prevent the ship from falling off.

Aloft the topmen clung to the yards waiting to take another reef if necessary.

It was a wicked night to have to be on deck, much less aloft, but Captain Perry decided it would not do for him to go below, especially with a new crew on board.

He had the men at the helm, the topmen, and the hands in the chains relieved frequently, but that didn't keep them any drier than the rest of the crew. Oliver, and the rest of the seamen who were standing by for orders, could protect themselves somewhat from the rain coming over the stern of the ship, but when she pitched into a trough, the following sea blocked the wind and allowed the spray to sweep aft from the bow.

Captain Perry had two choices. He could bring

the ship about and ride out the storm or he could keep going and run the risk of the ship's being pooped by the following sea. But he was of the old school, which felt that a captain should use his wind when he had it, and so the *General Greene* continued to bowl down the Atlantic Coast. It was a difficult decision for him to make, for he was responsible for his ship and men and at the same time he was nearly a month late in getting to his station at Havana. So Captain Perry took the chance and kept going.

Oliver could see the main- and foremasts from where he was huddled and he could scarcely keep his eyes off them. Back and forth they whipped as the ship lurched its way south. The creakings and groanings which she uttered as she was alternately pummeled by wind and water were lost in the roar of the combat, but none had to be an able-bodied seaman to know that any moment the rigging might part. Time and again Oliver peeked around the hatch to seek reassurance from his father. He got it, for every time he looked, there was his father, hands behind his back, staring at the rigging without a sign of fear on his face.

Toward six bells of the watch the figure of a sailor was seen struggling aft. As he grabbed the afterhatch for support Oliver could see that it was the carpenter's mate. Then after what seemed like minutes the wind carried fragments of a conversation to Oliver's ears.

"Seams . . . opening . . . water . . . hold. Start . . . pumps."

It was only because the carpenter's mate and Captain Perry had been forced to shout at each other that Oliver had been able to hear anything.

Toward morning the wind began to whip every which way and the men at the wheel had even more trouble holding the *General Greene* on her course.

"Center of storm . . ." Oliver heard Lieutenant Palmer shout.

Later the wind began to back from north to north by west and then north-northwest. The rain lessened and the port watch was ordered below, not, however, before they had shaken out the topsail reefs and loosed the staysails. With the danger past, Captain Perry was going to make the most of the dying wind.

By evening the *General Greene* was about due east from Cape May on the New Jersey coast. One hundred and twenty miles she had logged in eighteen hours. Then as the sun sank in the west the wind fell off completely.

With the pressure off her sides and masts, the *General Greene* stopped leaking somewhat, but the pumps still had to be manned. Further inspection showed that some of the provisions had been damaged by water and later it was found that it was impossible to stop the leaks completely. For a while Captain Perry considered going into the nearest port, but finally decided against it.

To make matters worse, the wind failed to pick up and for days the *General Greene* barely had steerageway. It was June 18th when she finally left the Florida coast and shaped her course for Havana. Once there, Captain Perry hoped he would be able to iron out his troubles.

But more troubles cropped up before he could do much about the ones he already had. At noon of June 18th, the surgeon's mate appeared on the quarter-deck.

"Four of the men are violently sick, sir," he reported. "They have high fevers."

"Fever," repeated Captain Perry with a start. "Not yellow fever, I hope?"

"It's hard to say, sir. We're inclined to believe the trouble came from stores damaged by the water we are shipping."

"Who are the men?"

"Four marines, sir."

Captain Perry thought a moment. "Well," he finally said, "make them as comfortable as possible and take every precaution against the spread of the disease. It may be contagious."

"Aye, aye, sir."

"And don't fail to come to me if there is anything you want done," Captain Perry added.

"Aye, aye, sir. It might be well to check the stores for damaged goods, if I may suggest it, sir."

"Very well. I'll speak to the steward at once."

The next day the marines were better and Captain Perry heaved a sigh of relief. "We're in poor enough condition as it is," he remarked to Lieutenant Palmer, "without having the crew attacked by fever."

But the *General Greene* was still a good way

from Havana and the climate was getting sulkier
and sulkier. Two days later three more marines fell
sick. Their symptoms were even more violent than
the first had been.

"We must get at the cause of this at once,"
Captain Perry told the ship's surgeon when informed of the trouble. "Have you any idea what it
might be?"

"The victims have all been men sleeping near
the pumps, sir," replied Dr. Tibbetts. "The ballast
might be the cause. There is a very putrid odor in
the hold now that the water has worked on the slate."

Captain Perry called the lieutenant of the
marines.

"Mr. Weaver, I want you to move your men
to the spar deck," he ordered. "I suggest you sleep
them in the waist. If it rains they'll have to sleep
on the gun deck as best they can. At least they'll
get some fresh air while it's pleasant."

"Aye, aye, sir."

Then Captain Perry turned to the officer of the
deck.

"Mr. Palmer, I want the men at the pumps
relieved every fifteen minutes. Also see that the hold
is disinfected with vinegar. You are to place yourself at the disposal of Dr. Tibbetts and follow out
any orders he may give toward stopping the spread
of this fever."

"Aye, aye, sir."

The next day one of the marines died and that
afternoon his body was committed to the sea. It was
now evident that the dreaded yellow fever had taken

a firm hold on the crew. Eight more marines and the midshipman in charge of the hold were entered on the sick list.

Oliver had been prepared for almost anything when he put to sea, but not this. It was terrifying to lie awake at night, hearing the men moan and wondering who would be the next victim. During the day it was not so bad for the men were kept busy trying to stop the spread of the disease. Everything Captain Perry and Dr. Tibbetts could think of was tried—in vain. One by one the men began to drop off. Almost every day Captain Perry had to go through the simple burial ceremony.

By July 1st, the *General Greene* was off the harbor of Havana and Captain Perry called his officers to his cabin.

"Gentlemen," he said, "my orders do not permit me to go into this port, but I might add that my orders do not take into consideration an epidemic of yellow fever. Hence, I consider it my duty to the crew to go into port at once and get all the help I can. Before taking this step, however, I feel that I must protect myself by having you sign this statement supporting my action."

Captain Perry handed the paper to Thomas Laing, the first lieutenant. Laing read it and signed. Then in order of rank, the other officers followed suit, including the second and third lieutenants, the lieutenant of the marines, the sailing master, and an acting lieutenant. As soon as all had signed Captain Perry dismissed them.

The effect of the fresh water and provisions had

an instantaneous effect on the crew. Perhaps it was psychological. At least Oliver was relieved to find no green scum in the water for a change.

So Captain Perry proceeded to cruise in the vicinity of Havana in search of French privateers. The possibility of an engagement kept the men keyed up for a while, but gradually as the days wore on and the water became slack again, the fever cropped up. Finally Captain Perry returned to Havana, picked up a convoy and headed for home.

"Maybe if we get out of this hot climate, we can check the fever," he said, and once again he justified his action by getting a signed statement from the surgeon's mate.

It was just as well that the *General Greene* met no incident on the voyage home, for by the end of July, when she dropped anchor in Newport Harbor, Oliver had seen his father perform the burial ceremony twenty times.

CHAPTER TWELVE

Second Cruise

FOR NINE DAYS THE *General Greene* LAY AT ANCHOR in Newport Harbor, waiting for the Town Council to lift quarantine restrictions and the crew spent the time wondering which was worse, enduring the rainy season of the West Indies or being so near to home and yet unable to get there. There also was the fear of being taken down by the fever; but, although a few of the crew took sick after the ship had anchored, none died.

Finally at the beginning of August, Oliver quit the ship and started his leave of absence. He boarded the ferry for Narragansett alone, for his father had to stay behind and look after his ship and men.

It was a much different Oliver Hazard Perry who landed at North Pier and started to climb to the village on top of Tower Hill. He was taller, straighter, and heavier and he walked with the roll of a man who was accustomed to having a sea under his feet. His uniform had something to do with the change, too, although his experience at sea had given him an air of confidence that belied his fourteen years.

Tower Hill had changed, too, for the house to which Oliver made his way was the old Squire

Case homestead in which Master Kelly had once taught school. Now the Perrys were living in it, and they were changed as well. Mrs. Perry treated Oliver more like a guest than a son, for she had lived by the sea long enough to know that naval officers didn't like to have mothers blubbering over them.

To his brothers and sisters, Oliver was now a personage, not just a member of the family. The uniform helped to create this feeling and then, too, Oliver was not above dropping a French or Spanish phrase now and then to make the illusion complete.

For a month he lazed about the house, humoring his brothers and sisters by taking part in their blueberry expeditions and in general playing the man of importance. Yet even the novelty of this eventually wore off and Oliver began looking more and more out to sea. His mother noticed it and nodded knowingly.

Meanwhile Captain Perry managed to get home now and again and the reports he brought concerning the reconditioning of the *General Greene* increased Oliver's restlessness. By September the ship had been fumigated from spar deck to hold, the slate ballast had been replaced with iron and the planking calked. She was about ready to resume her convoying duties off the Havana station.

But the first week in September brought a change in orders from the Secretary of the Navy. The *General Greene* was to take command of the squadron at Santo Domingo.

"It seems," said Captain Perry when Oliver reported for duty at Newport, "that there is a rebellion on the island and we have been ordered there to help curb it. So perhaps we shall see some real action this trip."

"What sort of rebellion?" asked Oliver, "And whom are we to help?"

"Some of the natives under a General Rigaud have risen up and are being opposed by a General Toussaint. The funny part about it is that they both are French. Rigaud, however, has been attacking American merchantmen, while Toussaint has been protecting them. Hence, we shall help Toussaint."

"I don't see how you are going to be able to tell them apart," said Oliver, "if both are French."

"Our job will be to stop every ship we see and examine her papers. Flags mean nothing in a war. Practically every ship has a whole set of flags of different nations, so as to be able to appear friendly or neutral as the occasion demands. The consul general at Cap-Français * will be able to tell us the true situation when we get to San Domingo. It may have changed before we arrive."

That was the longest conversation Oliver had with his father while the *General Greene* was in Newport. Captain Perry was on the go most of the time, rounding up his crew, conferring with Gibbs and Channing about supplies, and getting the ship ready for sea. It was not until September 23rd that the *General Greene* broke ground and headed south again.

The voyage was uneventful and even monoto-

* Now Cap-Haitien.

nous. Land was seldom seen and the ship encountered no severe weather. The only thing that kept Oliver occupied was learning to eat salt pork and beef again. A man had to have a hard stomach and a strong mind to put away the food on board a man-of-war.

"Just wait until the weevils start breeding in this bread," a messmate said at supper one afternoon. "Then we can break the monotony by racing them against each other."

But three weeks later, when Santo Domingo was raised, the weevils had not developed, although the bread was in such a state that the midshipmen were looking it over carefully before putting it into their mouths.

Oliver was on deck when the lookout spotted the coast and he scrambled forward to get a look. Far to the south he could see a bluish ridge of heavy shapeless lumps on the horizon. He was fortunate to be able to see it at all, for the sun was out for one of its few rainy season airings. As the hours went by, the blue turned to green and Oliver could make out masses of foliage. Clusters of palm trees and spreading mahogany trees stood out here and there and above them rose the mountains. The difference between this land and Rhode Island's treeless coast was astounding. Oliver had never seen anything like it, not even in Cuba.

That night the *General Greene* anchored off the harbor of Cap-Français and the next morning took aboard a pilot, who brought the ship safely into port. At once Captain Perry ordered his gig over and went ashore, taking Oliver with him.

It was the first time Oliver had stepped on foreign soil, for despite the number of times the *General Greene* had stopped at Havana, Oliver had

never been allowed to go ashore for fear he might contract yellow fever.

Having obtained directions from the pilot, Oliver and his father made their way through the muddy streets to the more substantial residence of the American consul general, Edward Stevens.

Captain Perry did not have to wait long to see Stevens, for as soon as his name had been taken in, the consul came striding out of his office with hand outstretched.

"Welcome, Captain Perry," he said. "Come right in." Then noticing Oliver, he stopped and smiled. "And this is . . . ?"

"Midshipman Oliver Perry, my son," Captain Perry explained.

"Delighted," said Stevens. "Won't you step right in?"

Once inside the office Stevens apologized for its disheveled appearance. "Haven't been here too long myself," he said, with a smile. Then, after asking a few questions about their voyage, he settled down to the business at hand.

"I presume you have a rough idea of what is taking place here," he began.

Captain Perry nodded.

"We are in the strange position of fighting two types of French and aiding a third. The reason we are trying to help Toussaint is that so far he has respected all neutrals, whereas Rigaud has no scruples whatsoever. In fact, I would call him a pirate. While he is making war on Toussaint, his ships are attacking shipping all along the coast. For the most part he has nothing but barges. These lie in wait until a vessel is becalmed and then they attack and plunder it. Toussaint, of course, is trying to destroy these barges, and the more he destroys of them the less is the danger to our merchantmen and those of other neutrals. Hence, it is only logical that, despite the fact Toussaint is French, we should help him. I might add that the British feel the same way about it."

"Where do we come in?" asked Captain Perry.

"I am coming to that," said Stevens, leaning back in his chair and pairing his finger tips. "The point I want to make clear first, however, is that so far our affairs with General Toussaint have been most harmonious and I think it is to the interest of our country to keep them that way."

Stevens looked at Captain Perry before continuing.

"Now I should like to see our American captains co-operate with the general in any way possible, notably in the matter of destroying Rigaud's barges. A short time ago we—that is, the British agent and myself—agreed to let Toussaint fit out a number of armed vessels to protect his coasting trade from Rigaud. That was before our ships arrived on the scene. Now that we have gone that far, I think it would be well to continue to help Toussaint to the extent of wiping out Rigaud. The president, of course, concurs, and so we shall allow Toussaint to keep his vessels."

"In what way may they be identified?" asked Captain Perry.

"Each of Toussaint's ships carries a passport signed by the British agent and myself. Now, are there any other questions?"

"Yes," replied Captain Perry. "My orders from the secretary suggested that I cruise rather than convoy on this station. Do you think that is wise?"

"I do," said Stevens. "If you convoy you necessarily leave part of the coast open to attack, whereas if you cruise Rigaud and the French privateers never know where and when to expect you."

"One more question. What United States ships are on this station now?"

"The frigate *Boston*, Captain Little, and the brig *Norfolk*, Lieutenant Bainbridge. The *George Washington*, Captain Fletcher, was here, but she was found to be too slow for cruising purposes. Captain Talbot is expected shortly in the *Constitution*."

"Good men, all of them," said Captain Perry, "but I'll be especially willing to give up the command of this station when Captain Talbot arrives. Captured British privateers during the last war, he did, then spent the rest of the time in prison. He was another one of us to rot in the prison ship *Jersey* in New York harbor. Only he didn't escape. He finished the war in Dartmoor after having been given a taste of the Old Sugar House in New York. Comes from Providence, you know, thirty miles or so from where I live."

"Indeed," said Stevens. "Well, I guess you weren't the only Rhode Islanders to get a taste of British prisons during the Revolution."

"Nor the only navy men either," replied Captain Perry. "Preble visited the *Jersey*. He served under Captain Little on the *Winthrop*. Lieutenant Hull's father was a prisoner on the *Jersey*, too."

Stevens then tactfully terminated the conversation. "Nothing else you want to know is there?"

"Nothing, thank you," replied Captain Perry. "All I need are a few stores from the navy agent here. It is a strange war, though. I guess we'll have to go on the theory that not all Frenchmen are bad Frenchmen."

"It is not only strange, but bewildering," said Stevens, with a smile. "You can imagine my predicament, trying to decide what is best for our government." Then with the graciousness of a diplomat, he showed his visitors to the door and pointed out the way to the navy agent.

"Good luck," he said as he shook hands with Oliver and his father. "I hope you capture lots of Frenchmen—the bad ones, I mean."

SHIP'S CUTTER

CHAPTER THIRTEEN

Speaking a Brig

EVEN WHEN THE *General Greene* WAS LYING IN PORT taking on provisions as she was doing now, Oliver continued to learn things an officer should know. He'd been in the navy for six months, two of them at sea, and in all that time he had done little but absorb information. And it seemed to him that if he stayed in the navy the rest of his life he never would learn all there was to running a man-of-war.

Yet that was his job. As a midshipman he was looked upon as a student, more than a member of the crew. He was an officer in embryo and as a consequence his assignments varied. One day he would be on the quarter-deck at the beck and call of the captain or the officer of the deck. Another time he would be in charge of the seaman cleaning the gun deck. Nominally he was in charge of the men, but actually he was there to learn all the things that had to be done to keep a man-of-war shipshape. Still another day he would be in the fo'c'sle learning the intricate workings of the head sails. This was what he liked best because it let him be near Weaver, who knew as much about sailing a ship as any man aboard.

There were a thousand and one things Oliver

had learned from Weaver: how to use a gun for an extra anchor in a storm; how to back wind a jib to help bring the ship about; how to trim sail to get the most out of the ship. But best of all he had learned what was meant when the bo'sun sang out, "Haul taut the lifts and trusses! Steady out the bo'lines!"

Oliver knew, too, that when a man went aloft to furl or reef, it was "one hand for the ship and one hand for yourself." Weaver had told him that the first time he went aloft, but there was one thing Weaver had cannily omitted.

No sooner had Oliver reached the masthead than the midshipman in charge of the top had said:

"Mr. Perry, is this your first time aloft?"

"Aye, sir."

"Then I'm afraid you'll have to pay for your footing."

"I don't understand, sir."

"It is customary for every man who goes aloft for the first time to buy a mug of grog for all hands."

Oliver had smiled and replied, "I don't like to strike my colors without a fight, but I'm afraid I'm badly outnumbered."

"That you are, sir."

And Oliver had paid.

Nor had he escaped having his hammock cut out from under him and all the other devilish things the midshipmen did to each other to break the monotony. One thing he had avoided so far, however, was being strung up to a yardarm by the ankles. Once in a while a midshipman might be found asleep on deck during a watch and if some of his messmates were idle they might be tempted to slip a noose around his ankles and hoist him up. So far Oliver had been able to keep awake during his turn on deck. Sometimes it had been hard work, but by beating his arms against his body and by walking back and forth on deck he had managed to shake his drowsiness. Besides, Oliver preferred to read if he had nothing else to do. An officer never could know too much, his father had told him. Even now, while the *General Greene* was lying in Cap-Français harbor, Oliver kept at his studies. At sea there were liable to be too many interruptions and the *General Greene* would put to sea soon.

Two days later she weighed anchor and started her cruise along the coast. Perhaps now she would see some action. There seemed to be a slight tension in the crew, for action meant enemy ships and enemy ships meant prize money, providing, of course, your ship was the victor.

Four leagues out from Cap-François there came a yell from the masthead:

"Sail, ho! Sail to leeward!"

Captain Perry sprang from the quarter-deck to the mizzen shrouds hoping to get a look at the sail, but seeing nothing he called to the lookout:

"What do you make her to be?"

"Brig, sir," came the reply. "Sailing about northwest."

Captain Perry jumped back to the deck where Lieutenant Laing was awaiting orders.

"Bear up to her, if you please, Mr. Laing. I'll

have the staysails set too, and you may turn up all hands."

"Aye, aye, sir."

Captain Perry kept staring to leeward, waiting for a glimpse of the sail. When he wasn't keeping his vigil, he was shouting to the lookout:

"Masthead there."

"Aye, sir."

"Keep an eye peeled for another sail."

"Aye, aye, sir."

"And let me know as soon as the brig changes its course."

"Aye, aye, sir."

Presently the distant sail could be seen from the deck of the *General Greene* and Captain Perry, his glass glued to the distant patch of white, ordered the starboard guns run out. From below came a rumbling as the heavy 12-pounders were rolled into place.

At first only the brig's topgallant sails could be seen from the deck, but as the ships converged Oliver could make out her lower sails. When her decks could be seen, Captain Perry ordered the colors run up. As the Stars and Stripes fluttered to the peak the stranger showed for the first time that she had noticed the *General Greene*. She broke out the tricolor of France. A murmur rose from the crew.

"Acting rather strange for a Frenchman," Oliver heard Lieutenant Laing say to Captain Perry.

"Might be one of Toussaint's ships. Fire a gun to windward, if you please."

A 12-pounder belched from the bow and a cloud of white drifted away on the wind. Promptly the stranger came about.

"That's more like it," said Captain Perry and he wore the *General Greene* so that when she hove

GUN DECK OF A FRIGATE

to her starboard guns were pointing right at the stranger. It was no idle threat, for on the deck below the gunners were just waiting for the order to blow their matches and fire.

Captain Perry, picking up his speaking trumpet and stepping to the rail, shouted:

"Ahoy! What brig is that?"

The reply was partially lost in the wind.

"Say it again," roared Captain Perry.

Still the officers on the *General Greene* couldn't catch the name.

"Sounded like 'Anne' to me, sir," said Lieutenant Laing.

"I'll send a boat," bellowed Captain Perry across the water and then, turning to Laing, he said, "My gig, if you please, and pass the word for Mr. Perry to come with me."

Oliver bounded to the starboard gangway, noticed that his father was buckling on his sword and wondered if he should get his own short one.

"Haven't time now," Captain Perry replied when Oliver asked him, and at once began to descend the ladder. The gig, rising and falling with each swell, was awaiting him below. Captain Perry waited for the gig to rise again and then jumped neatly into the stern sheets. Oliver followed him.

"Give way," ordered Captain Perry, and the crew put its oars against the ship and pushed off.

Up and down the gig inched its way toward the brig with Captain Perry and Oliver silently watching the quarter-deck. Now they could see the faces of the crew, mostly black and brown.

"Oars," ordered Captain Perry and the gig eased alongside. A boatswain's chair was lowered and in a jiffy the two officers were on deck.

A swarthy officer came forward.

"Captain Dufour, brig *Elan,* Colony of San Domingo," he said, showing two rows of white, even teeth.

"Captain Perry of the United States ship *General Greene.*"

There was a pause. Then, remembering Oliver,

Captain Perry added, "My son, Midshipman Perry." The three officers shook hands.

"Now, sir, what can we do for you?" Captain Dufour spoke with a decided accent.

"I should like to see your papers, if you please."

"Of course." Captain Dufour led the way aft to his cabin. Once inside he withdrew a packet of papers from his desk and handed them to Captain Perry. The latter opened the papers one by one and read them without comment. At last he came to the one he wanted, the passport signed by Stevens, the American consul general, and by Douglas, the British agent. Finally he spoke:

"Your papers are in order, sir, and I am sorry that I had to stop you. However, since we are interested in helping General Toussaint and the Colony of San Domingo, perhaps it is just as well. What can you tell me of the situation?"

"My ship and all the others that have been placed in commission by General Toussaint are interested only in capturing the barges of Rigaud. These are now stationed chiefly in the Bight of Léogane on the west side of the island."

"How about French privateers?" asked Captain Perry.

"They do not bother this island. They are located mostly to the east of Puerto Rico and the Windward Islands. The British cruisers have control of the southern part of San Domingo and your American ships have chased the privateers from the northern coast of the island."

"What would you suggest we do?"

"Help us capture the barges of Rigaud in the Bight of Léogane. The barges keep close to shore until a commercial vessel becomes becalmed. Then they strike, but you must be careful there too, for there are many calms in the bight."

"Well," said Captain Perry finally, "Captain Talbot of the United States frigate *Constitution* is expected soon to take command on this station and I shall relay this information to him. I am sure he will be pleased to have it."

With that the Perrys took their leave and returned to the *General Greene*.

When Oliver went to supper that afternoon at the start of the dog watch, he sensed something wrong with his messmates. They had stopped their chatter as soon as he had appeared at the table. Oliver stood the silence as long as he could and finally turned to the boy beside him.

"What's wrong?" he asked.

The boy shrugged his shoulders. "Ask Tew. He's the one who has been doing all the talking."

Oliver looked at the senior midshipman.

"Well, sir, what is it?"

Tew laid his knife and fork down and rested his arms on the table.

"I'll tell you what the trouble is," he said evenly. "We're all sick and tired of seeing you picked every time the captain goes on an important errand. What's the matter with the rest of us? We want to learn what's going on just as much as you do."

Oliver bit his lip. This was a ticklish situation. Midshipmen had dueled over less than this.

"And another thing," Tew continued. "We don't like the way this ship is disciplined. A captain has no right to send a petty officer to call a midshipman. Let him send an officer of equal or superior rank like they do on any good ship."

Oliver was silent for a moment. It really was none of his business and yet he had to live with these officers. He had to make some gesture.

"I don't see why you take it out on me," he finally said. "It's not my fault. However, I'll be willing to go to my father and present your case—without mentioning any names, of course."

"That's exactly what we'd like you to do," replied Tew.

The rest of the meal was eaten in silence and when it was over Oliver went directly to his father's cabin where he presented the facts of the case.

Captain Perry's eyes narrowed as Oliver told his story.

"Who's the ringleader? Tew?"

"I'm sorry, sir," Oliver said. "I promised not to mention any names."

Captain Perry thought a moment. "All right," he finally said. "You go back and tell that bunch of lazy louts that as long as I'm captain of this ship I'll run it as I please. When they become captains they can run their ships the same way."

CHAPTER FOURTEEN

Bad News

FOR TWO MONTHS THE *General Greene* STAYED IN the vicinity of Cap-Français, despite the fact that Captain Perry knew that most of the French privateers had been chased away from San Domingo. Yet it was not his fault, for he had relayed the information to Captain Silas Talbot when the *Constitution* had arrived in the middle of October to take command of the squadron on the station.

The most the *Constitution* had done since she arrived was to beat a British frigate in an all-day race for a cask of Madeira wine. The only change in strategy that Talbot had made was to split the squadron and assign each ship to a specific cruising ground. The *General Greene* was sent north of Cap-Français to the eastern end of the Bahama Islands; the *Boston,* Captain Little, was ordered northwest of Cap-Français; the *Norfolk,* Lieutenant Bainbridge, went to the northeast; and the *Constitution* remained in the vicinity of Cap-Français.

Yet all the *General Greene* encountered were merchantmen. Day after day she weaved in and out of the islands, sometimes going as long as forty-eight hours without seeing a sail.

It was not until November that she captured

her first prize and that without a struggle. The ship was a brig, flying Danish colors, and she came to on the first warning shot. However, the *Industry*, as the name of the brig turned out to be, looked more French than Danish to Captain Perry and he put a prize crew aboard her under the charge of Midshipman George W. Tew and ordered her back to Newport.

The only satisfaction that Oliver obtained from the business, outside of the thrill of chasing a strange sail, was a chance to try out his French on some of the prisoners the *General Greene* carried into Cap-Français.

In all the *General Greene* made four captures during the last two months of the year and not one of the ships needed more than a shot across the bow to stop her. Toward the end of November she took a Danish schooner bound from Gonaïves to St. Thomas, but soon released it on the orders of Captain Talbot. On December 1st, she was in company with the *Boston*, when the latter took the brig *Flying Fish* and retook the American schooner *Weymouth*, which had been captured by the French.

Yet if the members of the crew of the *General Greene* complained for want of prizes and action, they were not alone, for the crews of the other American ships in the West Indies had little more to keep them busy and happy.

To make matters worse, the *General Greene* began to open up her seams and in the middle of December she was ordered into Cap-Français for repairs. There she stayed for a whole month, while the crew loafed about wondering which they would catch first, yellow fever or a prize.

The situation was not improved by the announcement which the consul general brought aboard in the middle of January. Captain Parry gasped when he read it and sat a long time in his cabin before going on deck.

"You may call all hands aft," he said to Lieutenant Laing when he had reached the quarter-deck.

While the men were gathering Captain Perry stood with his hands behind his back looking out to sea. Laing had to speak to him to let him know that the men were waiting.

Captain Perry looked the men over before speaking. Then he finally said, "It's not very pleasant news I have for you. I'll read you the message as it has just been presented to me:

" 'General order to the officers of the United States Navy and Marines from the Secretary of the Navy.

" 'The President with deep affliction announces to the Navy and to the Marines, the death of our beloved citizen George Washington, Commander of our Armies and late President of the United States, but rendered more illustrious by his eminent virtues, and a long series of the most important services, than by the honors which his grateful country delighted to confer upon him—

" 'Desirous that the Navy and the Marines should express in common with every other description of American Citizens, the high sense which all feel of the loss Our Country has sustained in the death of this Good and Great Man, the President directs that the vessels of the Navy, in our own and foreign ports be put in mourning for one week, by wearing their colours half mast high, and that the officers of the Navy, and of the Marines, wear crepe on the left arm, below the elbow, for six months.

       "'Navy Dept. 20th Dec. 1799

        " 'Ben Stoddert' "

CHAPTER FIFTEEN

The Fall of Jacmel

IT WAS A STRANGE WAR THE UNITED STATES WAS fighting with France. The warships of each nation avoided each other constantly, because there was no money for the crews in capturing an enemy warship. They preferred to look for enemy merchantmen with rich cargoes. Actually the warships were nothing but privateers although the government took half the prize money obtained from the sale of the captured cargoes. Even so, there generally was four or five thousand dollars left to be divided among the crew.

The result of all this was that navy captains usually captured a ship first and let the courts worry about the legality of it afterward.

For young midshipmen like Oliver Hazard Perry it was good experience. They were going to school and getting well paid for it. But from the actions of the *General Greene* it looked as if Oliver would get more experience than money from the present cruise.

For the first two weeks of the new year, 1800, the *General Greene* cruised in company with the *Constitution* and *Boston* off Cap-Français. It was no fault of Captain Perry's that his ship was not assigned to more lucrative work, for the *General Greene* was proving a disagreeable ship. Her seams were constantly opening and her rigging was in no condition to stand the strain of extra canvas.

Another thing that was keeping the United States squadron close to Cap-Français was the expected arrival of a fleet of French frigates. But that fleet had been expected for two months now, so finally Captain Talbot of the *Constitution* ordered the squadron to move on. The *General Greene* was sent north to Turk's Passage on the easterly end of the Bahamas to await any ships that might leave San Domingo after the United States squadron disappeared.

For two weeks the *General Greene* stayed as ordered in the passage and then returned to Cap-Français, spoke the *Constitution,* and started at once for a cruise around the island of San Domingo via St. Nicholas Mole on the western end.

If anybody knew how long the *General Greene* would be gone, Joseph Weaver would know and Oliver promptly put the question to him.

"Barring accident, sir, we should be back at Cap-Français in a month," said Weaver. "But you never can tell. We're liable to strike a lot of soft weather in the Bight of Léogane."

"Yes, I've heard some of the other men speak of the calms there."

"Probably worried about their time, sir," said Weaver. "My time runs out in April and I'd like to be home by then."

"Why so anxious? As soon as you get home you'll want to go to sea again."

"That's just the point, sir," said Weaver. "Begging your pardon, but I want to get another ship."

Oliver looked surprised. "What's the matter?" he asked sharply. "Aren't you being treated well enough?"

"Oh, it isn't that, sir," said Weaver. "I just think the *General Greene* is an unlucky ship. Nothing seems to go right with her. It's nobody's fault, mind you, sir. It's just—well, some ships are lucky and some aren't. Now you take the *Herald*, for instance; she's one of the oldest ships in the service, but she's never seen action and she's never even captured anything. That's what I mean, sir, it's nobody's fault but her own."

"I see," said Oliver. "What ship would you like to sail on?"

"The *Boston*, perhaps, sir. She's been in service less than a year and already she's taken as many prizes as any of the others."

Oliver had to admit that there was a lot in what Weaver had to say. The *General Greene* certainly had been a disappointment. Still, there was time for a change of luck. Perhaps now she was getting away from Cap-Français she'd get some action.

The *General Greene* worked her way westward, to the end of the island, bore southward through Windward Passage between San Domingo and Cuba and finally stopped at St. Nicholas Mole for water. Then she was off again, across the Bight of Léogane to Donna Maria and then eastward along the southern shore of San Domingo.

Meanwhile Captain Perry had picked up word from General Toussaint that the city of Jacmel on the southern coast of the island was under siege and that its surrender would be greatly hastened if a frigate like the *General Greene* would station herself in the vicinity and intercept supplies to the garrison in the city. Captain Perry at once began blockading the harbor and for nearly three weeks the *General Greene* cruised back and forth. If Rigaud's ships had had less respect for United States frigates, the *General Greene* might have seen some action, but as it was she merely scared everything out of sight, the way a dogfish scares mackerel.

The result was just as good as far as Toussaint was concerned. By the end of February, the garrison in Jacmel was about starved out and on that day the *General Greene* rolled out her guns and prepared to move within range of the city's forts. She was going to help Toussaint attack the garrison.

It was welcome news to the crew. Bombarding the forts would break the monotony of holystoning decks and tarring rigging and all the other tasks Captain Perry was continually thinking up to keep his men occupied. Oliver was excited at the prospect, but the closer the time came the sleepier he got. His stomach felt heavy. He didn't think he was afraid, he just wanted to get things started. He wondered if his father felt the same way.

There was no way of telling. Captain Perry looked just the same except perhaps for a few tighter lines around his mouth, and a gleam in his eye that Oliver hadn't noticed before.

The crew seemed more lively, too, jumping to orders as they scarcely had done since the cruise started. And there were plenty of orders to be carried out. The spar and gun decks were cleared, the surgeon and his mate laid out their saws and knives in the sick bay in the bow, the decks were covered with sand to keep them from getting slippery with blood. When all was ready Captain Perry gave the order to close in on the forts.

The defenders were ready. They had seen the preparations on the *General Greene* and long before she was in range puffs of white appeared from the gun posts. On came the *General Greene* until the 12-pounders on her gun deck were in range.

"Ready about," barked the officer of the watch and then, "Hard alee." The *General Greene* came up into the wind with her starboard guns leveled on the forts. "Fire when ready," ordered Captain Perry.

There was a pause as firing orders were given below and the flames from the matches ate their way down into the charges. Then came a succession of roars that shook the ship and the forts no longer were visible. From the gun deck Oliver could hear the gunners' mates' orders: "Sponge your guns" . . . "Wad to cartridge and ram home" . . . "Wad to shot and ram home" . . . "Man your side tackles" . . . "Run out your guns" . . . "Level your guns" . . . "Blow your matches" . . . "Fire!" Again came another roar, this time with more unison, and again the smoke covered up the view.

There was nothing for Oliver to do so he climbed into the starboard shrouds for a better view. It didn't occur to him that he was right in the line of fire. He was too anxious to see what damage had been done. The *General Greene*'s guns were getting the range but so were those of the fort. Oliver sud-

denly felt the rigging shake and looking up saw that a stay had been parted by a ball from one of the three forts. Still he clung to the shrouds.

For twenty minutes the *General Greene* kept up her fire, the broadsides coming more quickly as the guns warmed up. The quicker they came the more effective they were.

"We've silenced one gun," yelled Lieutenant Laing to no one in particular. Oliver doubted if the man knew he had spoken.

Still the balls from the forts came over, most of them falling short. A few passed above or through the rigging. Captain Perry had furled his sails to protect them. There was little likelihood of the ship's being attacked by Rigaud's barges that were lying close inshore. And if the ship were attacked Captain Perry still had his 6-pounders on the quarter-deck and fo'c'sle.

Gradually the shots falling around the *General Greene* became fewer and fewer. Gun by gun was being silenced in the forts. Then came a roar from the crew. The town was being given up. People could be seen scurrying to the safety of the forts. Ten more minutes of firing and down came the colors over one fort. The defenders ran for shelter in the second, but this only concentrated the *General Greene's* fire and in a few minutes the second fort fell. At the end of forty minutes all that remained in the fight was the third and strongest fort. This, too, hauled down its colors in short order and that gave Oliver a chance for action. Boats were ordered out and Oliver was put in charge of one of them. The plan was to secure the barges in the harbor and then enter the town.

Oliver no sooner had placed himself in the stern sheets when there came a shout from the deck above him.

"Sail ho!"

Oliver could see the men above him turn and look out to sea.

"Looks like a French frigate," Oliver heard Lieutenant Laing say to his father.

"It does at that," Captain Perry replied. "Call the men back, if you please. We'll have to get out where there is more wind and water."

Up came the boats and up went the anchor and sails and the *General Greene* left Toussaint and his men to take care of the mopping up around Jacmel. She had work of her own to do.

As Oliver watched the ships converge he could see that the Frenchman had the better of what wind there was. The *General Greene* would have to do some quick maneuvering to get her guns in position to do much damage. The crew also had plenty of work to do cleaning up the debris caused by the few shots the forts had landed.

Just when he was wondering when his father would come about, the approaching ship ran up her colors.

"British," the crew gasped as one.

"It may be a trick," Oliver heard his father say. " 'Bout ship, Mr. Laing. We'll cross her bow and then come about and cross her stern so we can speak her."

Over went the helm and the *General Greene* slid off on a port tack, but the Frenchman kept coming before the wind. As the *General Greene* crossed her bow Oliver could see that her gun ports were closed. Maybe she was a Britisher at that.

When the *General Greene* came back on the

starboard tack and hailed the stranger the point was proved. She was a French frigate all right, but she was now in possession of the British. Captain Perry gave orders to wear ship and the *General Greene* headed back to Jacmel.

Once in the harbor, Captain Perry ordered his gig over and went ashore to have a conference with General Toussaint. When he returned he was all smiles and ordered the whole crew aft.

"General Toussaint wishes me to thank you men," he said, "for your fine work and to show you his appreciation he is going to send you ten thousand pounds of coffee."

After the cheering had died down and the men had been dismissed Oliver walked forward to where Weaver was sitting.

"Well, Weaver," he said, "do you still think the *General Greene* is unlucky?"

Weaver stood up and tipped his cap. "Begging your pardon, sir, yes. It's nice to have the coffee, but for me, I'll take prize money instead."

CHAPTER SIXTEEN

Bluffing the British

WEAVER WAS FORCED TO CHANGE HIS OPINION ABOUT the *General Greene* shortly, for within two weeks after the fall of Jacmel she had captured a Danish schooner and an armed French schooner, both without argument. But the good luck lasted only the month it took the *General Greene* to complete her cruise about the island, for when she fell in with the *Constitution* off Cap-Français early in April, there was bad news awaiting her.

In the first place, there was word from the Secretary of Navy that there would be no prize money from the brig, *Flying Fish,* which the *General Greene* and *Boston* had captured. The court had not condemned the brig and had let her go. In the second place, Captain Talbot of the *Constitution* as commander of the squadron ordered Captain Perry to turn loose the French schooner he had brought with him from Jacmel.

Finally, since the time of most of the members of the *General Greene's* crew was about up, she was ordered to return home. First, however, she was to go into Cap-Français for water and repairs. Then she was to proceed to New Orleans, pick up General Wilkinson and his family, return to Havana and convoy any United States merchantmen to the United States.

Some good news was included in the reports from home. Congress had appropriated $2,000,000 for the building of six 74-gun frigates and the United States *Constitution* had fought a draw with the French frigate *La Vengeance*.

Once in port, the *General Greene* ran into more trouble. The repairs were not so simple as had been thought. Then Captain Talbot put seventeen invalids ashore with orders for Captain Perry to return them to the United States. Immediately twelve men of the *General Greene's* crew came down with fever. Next Captain Perry had difficulty obtaining a passport. Then when he was ready to sail he could get no one to pilot him out of the harbor. Finally General Toussaint arrivd in Cap-Français and asked Captain Perry to delay his sailing for forty-eight hours.

The only good that came of all this was the chance to transfer the seventeen invalids that Captain Perry had in his care to the prize schooner *Juno* which was leaving Cap-Français for the United States.

But Oliver enjoyed the stay in Cap-Français for the most part. He had numerous opportunities to go into the town and he enjoyed the ceremonies of welcoming General Toussaint on board. The *General Greene* had never had occasion to give a full Federal salute and she made the most of it. The ship *Herald,* which was also in port at the time, put on her full dress and fired a round from her guns.

What Oliver didn't like about the stay in Cap-Français was the dissension among the crew. Their time was up and they wanted to get home. It was not much fun for them to be cooped up in a stuffy ship in a hot foreign port when they were supposed to be home and paid off. A few deserted but the rest stayed on, probably figuring that the *General Greene* would get them home as quickly as any other ship.

After twenty-one days in port the *General Greene* finally weighed anchor. At that she had to be towed out of the harbor for want of wind.

A month later the *General Greene* had picked up General Wilkinson and his family at New Orleans and had started back to Havana with an American brig in convoy. Nothing happened until the ships had reached the coast of Cuba where a British ship of the line came up out of the horizon. When she had established her identity Captain Perry paid her no more attention until suddenly he heard a shot. The British had fired across the brig's bow.

Captain Perry whirled. "Damn his impudence! Mr. Laing! Call the men to quarters! Mr. Palmer! Signal the brig to hold her course! Mr. Fenner! You may run out your guns!"

The deck of the *General Greene* became a bedlam. Tackling a big British frigate like this one was not to be taken lightly, but Oliver knew and so did the rest of the men that, while Christopher Perry might have a few drawbacks as a captain, lack of courage was not one of them. On the other hand, the *General Greene* had one advantage. She would be easier to handle in this light air than the Britisher would.

Captain Perry stood facing aft waiting for the frigate's next move. He took it for granted his orders were being carried out. It was just as well, for he was almost too mad to see. But he still had himself under control and when the frigate lowered a longboat he whipped his orders over his shoulder without taking his eye from the scene.

" 'Bout the ship, Mr. Laing! Fire a shot across the bow of that longboat when you are ready."

The *General Greene* came around and when the 6-pounders on the quarter-deck were in range one was fired. The shot had two effects. It caused the boat to heave to and at the same time it brought the frigate bearing down on the *General Greene*.

Oliver could see the British captain in his elaborate uniform getting ready to hail the quarter-deck and he decided he was glad he didn't have to sail under that old grouch. When the frigate was alongside the captain hailed the *General Greene*. There were no formalities. He was too mad.

"Why has my longboat been fired upon?" he roared.

Captain Perry gave him as good as he sent. "To prevent it from boarding my brig."

"It's damned funny one of His Majesty's seventy-four-gun ships can't board an American brig!"

"If she were a first-rate ship she should not do

so to the dishonor of my flag!" roared Captain Perry
in reply.

By this time the British ship had got out of
hailing distance. Oliver expected her to come back
again, but she didn't. Instead she picked up her
longboat and went her way.

SHIP'S LONG GUN (BELOW DECKS)

CHAPTER SEVENTEEN

Home Again

BY THE TIME THE *General Greene* REACHED HAVANA, toward the end of June, Oliver was ready to go home. So was the rest of the crew. Enlistments had run out and the men were beginning to find fault. The fact that the rainy season had returned to the West Indies didn't help matters, either.

The *General Greene* was proving more than unlucky for Oliver; it was becoming disagreeable. Things might not have been so bad if Captain Perry had not antagonized the midshipmen, but he had, and Oliver had to endure the silence of his messmates. The trouble was that both parties had cause for grievance. The midshipmen had acted unruly and Captain Perry had been oppressive with them. He had even had one midshipman flogged. Yet it was not Oliver's affair, and the silence he was forced to endure was more than coincidental. Time and again he would come upon a group of midshipmen with their heads together and each time they would stop talking at his approach. It was the same at mealtimes. When Oliver was present there just wasn't anything for the other midshipmen to talk about.

The rest of the crew acted similarly but Oliver

knew what their trouble was. The crew was dis-
gruntled because there would be little if any prize
money coming to them at the end of the trip. They
were complaining that the *General Greene* spent too
much valuable time in port when she might be out
capturing prizes. And they seemed to blame Captain Perry for not finding any prizes to capture.
Captain Perry was even being held responsible for

SAILORS' MESS

the fever that had broken out on the first voyage
and the men were grumbling that there would be
a second epidemic if the *General Greene* did not
put for home soon.

It was a hard job keeping the men under control, but when Captain Perry took aboard a load of
pigs at Havana for his father's farm it looked for a
time as though the midshipmen at least were going
to mutiny.

"I signed on a man-of-war, not a merchantman," Oliver heard one of them say. "You can wager I'll make sure what I get next time."

The seamen took a different attitude. They were worried that the pigs would produce another fever epidemic. Oliver didn't hear this directly, but it was difficult to keep much secret when 200-odd men were cooped up on two small decks. Even the pigs seemed to appreciate the situation.

And there was plenty of time for the rumor to spread, since Captain Perry spent four days contacting merchantmen that wished to be convoyed and supplying his ship for the trip home.

It was a sorry mess for all concerned. It would have been bad enough if the *General Greene* had sailed dirctly for Newport, but convoying twelve ships made matters even worse. Back and forth the *General Greene* shuttled, now waiting for the slow sailors, now trying to keep the leaders in check. Then, to climax the business, the whole convoy became becalmed off the Virginia Capes.

For three days the ships lolled under a sun so hot that after five men had been prostrated the rest refused to go on deck. Any work that was to be done had to wait until nighttime. The canvas spread above the spar deck helped some as far as prostrations were concerned, but that was all. To relieve the situation Captain Perry had water let into the hold and then pumped out again. The gun deck was washed frequently and the whole ship fumigated and sprinkled with vinegar. Captain Perry was worrying about yellow fever as much as prostrations.

Finally on the fourth day the wind returned, but it was too late as far as one seaman was concerned. Already his skin had begun to turn yellow and he had that other symptom of the fever, violent vomiting. The next day two more men became ill and by the third day the total had risen to seven. Once again the *General Greene* was racing against time for the sake of the crew and once again she lost. Four days out of Newport the first body was committed to the sea and two days later the second. Finally, on July 21st, the five men left in sick bay heard the order to drop anchor and they knew they were in Newport Harbor once again.

For forty-eight hours the *General Greene* was under quarantine and then most of the crew was paid off and the officers given leave of absence. All but Captain Perry departed for home. He had considerable on his mind. There was the fever to check, the ship to be refitted at once, the pigs to be delivered to South Kingstown, and, most important, the Secretary of Navy wanted to see him in Washington, the new home of the United States government.

So again Oliver made his way alone to Tower Hill. Nor did he see much of his father that summer, for as usual the *General Greene* was causing trouble. Workmen were not anxious to go aboard the fever-ridden ship and consequently the fumigating and repairing went slowly. The repairs were considerable too, for Captain Perry wanted a false keel put on the *General Greene* so that she would handle better.

There certainly was no doubt now that the *General Greene* was an unlucky ship. While she had had practically no prize money to show for her cruise, Oliver learned that the schooner *Enterprize,* Lieutenant Commander Shaw, had taken eight French ships with the loss of only twelve men.

It was an ideal time for Oliver to be beached, for there was fishing and swimming and berrying and any number of things for him. to do to while away the time. Yet somehow he didn't enjoy all those things as much as he thought he would. There were two reasons for this. First of all, he was serious for his fifteen years of age; then again, his father's trip to Washington worried him. Captain Perry had said little about his talk with Secretary Stoddert, but Oliver knew that something unpleasant was in the wind.

By the middle of September he knew. A court of inquiry had been called at Newport by Secretary Stoddert to consider the conduct of Captain Perry on his last cruise.

For a whole day the court pondered the four charges: keeping the *General Greene* in Cap-Fran- çais for nearly a month after Captain Talbot had ordered him to sail; accepting 10,000 pounds of coffee from General Toussaint; cruelty to his mid- shipmen; endangering the lives of the crew by ship- ping a load of swine for his father's farm.

Worse than the suspense of wondering what the decision of the court would be was the two-month wait to hear the sentence of the president. The court had convened October 13th, and it was not until

December that Oliver learned the verdict. His father returned one night to Tower Hill and as soon as he entered the house Oliver looked at him questioningly. Captain Perry wearily sat down in a chair without even bothering to take off his coat. Slowly he drew a letter from his pocket and handed it to his wife.

Mrs. Perry unfolded it and read it slowly. Oliver could tell the tone of the letter from the way his mother bit her lower lip. Suddenly she flung the letter aside and threw her arms around her husband.

Oliver picked up the letter and read:

> Washington, D.C.
> Nav. Dep. 28th Nov. 1800

Captain Christopher R. Perry

Sir, the President of the United States, after having attentively considered the proceedings of the Court of Enquiry into your conduct, agrees with the Court in opinion, that you did not at Cape François, pay prompt or proper attention to the orders of your commanding officer: that you have been remiss in your duty in not causing the observance of discipline on board of the *General Greene*—and that the punishment you suffered to be inflicted on some of the Midshipmen was without law, contrary to the usage of the sea service; but believing you to be a brave man and a skillful officer—and qualified to render important service to your country, the President has determined to pass over this irregular and improper conduct, without inflicting any other punishment than suspending you for three months from your command in the Navy, during which time you will receive no pay nor other emolument from the

United States. The time of suspension to take place from the day of your delivery of the *General Greene* to Captain Campbell—who is the bearer of this—and who is sent on to take command of the ship.

I have the honour to be

Sir, your most obedient servant

Benjamin Stoddert

CHAPTER EIGHTEEN

A Vote for the Navy

THE SUSPENSION OF HIS FATHER WAS A SHOCK TO Oliver even though he had anticipated far worse punishment during the two-month wait for the sentence. He wondered how it would affect his own career. Would Captain Campbell want him for the *General Greene* or would he have to take a berth on some other ship? His curiosity got the better of him and he went to Newport to inquire into the situation.

Gibbs and Channing, the navy agents, usually knew everything that was going on, so Oliver made their Thames Street office his first port of call. There he received another shock. No sooner had he stepped into the office than Mr. Gibbs took him by the elbow and led him to an inner officer.

"I don't suppose I should tell you this," he said, relishing his morsel of information to the utmost, "but from a letter I received this morning you might just as well go home and pack that nice uniform of yours in a trunk."

Oliver shot a puzzled glance at the merchant. What was he driving at?

"Secretary Stoddert has just written me," Mr. Gibbs went on tantalizingly, "ordering me to con-

tinue making repairs on the *General Greene,* but—"
here the merchant paused, like a cat waiting for
the mouse to move again—"he also ordered me to
stop buying provisions for her."

The frown on Oliver's brow deepened. Mr.
Gibbs took full satisfaction from this, flicked some
lint from his trouser leg and proceeded.

"It seems that Mr. Davie has just arrived in
Washington from Paris with a treaty."

"Treaty!" gasped Oliver. "I see. Then it's all
over."

"Practically," said Mr. Gibbs; "but of course
the treaty has to be approved by Congress."

"Congress will approve it," said Oliver. "The
thing I'm worried about is the navy. Do you think
that will be disbanded?"

"Hardly," said Mr. Gibbs, "or why would
Secretary Stoddert order me to continue repairing
the *General Greene?*"

"That's right," admitted Oliver, "and if they
keep the *General Greene* in service that means that
all the other ships of her tonnage probably will be
kept too."

"Quite likely."

Oliver was quiet for a moment. Then he said:
"I guess I might just as well go back to Tower
Hill. I came here to learn if I would ship on the
General Greene on her next cruise, but what you
have told me changes the whole situation. I wonder
how much of a navy will be maintained?"

"That's hard to say, but it's been my experience
that the people of this country seldom worry about

the future. I wouldn't be surprised if the navy was reduced drastically. As a matter of fact, it's been reduced already."

"How do you mean?"

"Well, nobody has heard from Captain Fletcher or his crew since May when they left for the West Indies in that French prize the *Insurgente* and I understand that the *Pickering*, Captain Hillar, is missing."

"Missing?"

"Yup, wouldn't be surprised if the ocean swallowed her too. It's happened before."

"Yes, I know," said Oliver quietly as he prepared to leave.

There was little for him to do now but sit and wait and discuss with his father the possibilities of being retained in the standing navy.

"It would be just like Congress to put the whole lot of us on the beach," said Captain Perry. "If the navy had any say in the matter it might be different, but you never can tell what Congress will do. I only hope someone points out the fact that the Barbary pirate business has never been definitely settled.

"And another thing, Jefferson has said he would cut defense costs when he takes office. I think Adams is in favor of a navy, but will Congress act while he is still in power? I don't know, the whole thing's beyond me."

So it went all winter. By occasional trips to Newport Oliver learned that recruiting for the *General Greene* had been stopped and that Captain

Campbell was waiting further orders from the Secretary of the Navy. He learned too of a new book on navigation by Nathaniel Bowditch and that Lieutenant Bainbridge had been made a captain and ordered to carry tribute to the Dey of Algiers in the former merchant ship *General Washington.*

  • Then suddenly, even before the treaty with France had been ratified, Congress passed a Naval Peace Establishment Act, retaining 13 frigates, 9 captains, 36 lieutenants, and 150 midshipmen. Word reached Tower Hill two weeks before the list of officers and ships retained was printed in the paper.

Oliver saw the paper before his father and after finding his own name among the midshipmen, began looking for his father's name among the captains. It wasn't there. Barry had been retained and Nicholson, Dale, Truxton, Morris, Murray, Sam Barron, Rodgers, Preble, James Barron, Bainbridge, Campbell and Tingey, but not Perry. The *General Greene* had been retained too, along with all the other frigates, but only six of the ships were to be kept in service. The other seven were to be laid up. That meant the *General Greene* would be used only in case of emergency.

The list provided Oliver and his father a subject of conversation for several days. Why had Captain Little of the *Boston* been dropped? When had Midshipman George Tew been made a lieutenant? What future did Oliver have in the navy now that only six ships were to be kept in service? Captain Perry was doubtful that there was a future in the navy. Oliver would be better off to enter the mer-

chant service and try to become a captain in the
East India trade.

The conversations were brought to a climax
early in April when Oliver received a letter from
Captain Campbell asking if he intended to remain
in the navy.

"You've had my opinion," Captain Perry answered when Oliver put the matter up to him, "but
you'll have to make your own decision."

Oliver nodded. "Well," he finally said, "there's
no doubt I would make more money in the East
India trade, but—I think I'll stay in the navy."

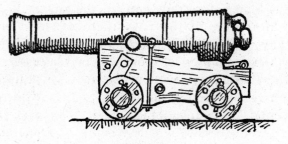

LONG GUN

CHAPTER NINETEEN

On the Beach

THE ARGUMENT IN THE PERRY HOUSEHOLD ABOUT THE
navy was no doubt reproduced in a good many New
England homes. As far as most naval men were concerned, to choose between the navy and the merchant marine was to choose between prestige and
profit. A great many naval men had both prestige
and profit, but most of them had inherited their
profits long before they entered the navy.

Moreover, in the navy there was the chance
for advancement. The navy was new, but its captains were old. Most of those who had been retained
by the Peace Establishment Act had Revolutionary
War records. Hence, according to Oliver's way of
thinking, a young midshipman shouldn't have
much trouble working his way up to a command,
providing he followed orders.

Christopher Perry couldn't see it that way,
especially after Jefferson had taken office.

"Mind you," he would say, "I'm not trying to
make you reverse your decision, but the government
isn't likely to spend anything on a navy when it
doesn't have to."

"Supposing we became involved in a war?"
Oliver would reply. "You admit yourself the Bar-

bary pirates business is not settled. Then Congress will have to increase the navy and those officers already enrolled will be at a great advantage."

"That's all very well and good," Christopher Perry would counter, "but if the British navy isn't big enough to whip the pirates, what chance has a miniature reproduction like ours? England and France and Spain have been paying tribute to the Barbary pirates for years and just because they do it we'll continue to do it too. Why, we're nothing but a bunch of copycats! Look at our navy—an exact replica of the British. We copied their rules, their customs, everything. We even set up a marine corps. Why? Just because the British had one, not because we needed one. England has a marine corps to keep her officers and seamen from killing each other. Lord knows we never have any trouble like that. Why, most of our officers and seamen went to school together. It so happens the marine corps idea worked out all right, because as you know yourself the marines come in right handy for landing parties and for musket work at close quarters. Still, the fact remains that we'll do whatever England does and that includes paying tribute to the Barbary pirates."

Oliver had to admit that what his father said was true, but it wouldn't be if he had anything to say about it. The United States Navy might have plenty of trouble conquering the British, but it certainly should be able to handle the small fleets of Algiers, Tunisia, Tripoli, and Morocco. And the English navy could lick the pirates too, but why hadn't it?

"Politics," replied Christopher Raymond Perry.

"England wants the Mediterranean trade and she wants it all to herself. She can afford to pay more for it than the other countries and consequently the Barbary pirates bother her ships less than they do the ships of the other countries trading in the Mediterranean."

"Then I should think it would pay the United States to send a fleet over there and clean up the mess once and for all. We haven't enough money to protect our merchant ships by tribute, but we certainly have a good enough navy to protect them by force."

"It would pay the United States to conquer the

Barbary pirates," said Christopher Raymond Perry, "but Jefferson doesn't think in terms of paying. He's penny-wise and pound-foolish."

And so it went for months, while Oliver waited to be assigned to duty. His father may have had the better of the arguments, but he was butting his head against a stone wall. Oliver had made up his mind once and for all.

Then things began to happen. No sooner had Jefferson taken office than the Bashaw of Tripoli decided that, since the American navy had been reduced, now was the time to seek more tribute. Besides, Tunis and Algiers had made much better deals with this new country.

Oliver had the laugh on his father when the president decided to send a fleet to the Mediterranean, but his father had the last laugh when it was learned that all the fleet was going to do was try to bluff the Bashaw of Tripoli into peace.

"Commodore Dale is a good man," observed Christopher Perry, "but his hands are tied. He hasn't even got authority to capture Tripolitan ships."

The fleet that was to sail to the Mediterranean included the *President,* Captain James Barron; *Philadelphia,* Captain Sam Barron; *Essex,* Captain William Bainbridge; and the *Enterprize,* Lieutenant Commander Andrew Sterrett, but before it could get under way trouble had started. The Bashaw of Tripoli had ordered that the flag over the United States consulate at Tripoli be cut down.

This was May, 1801, and a month later the United States declared war on Tripoli.

Now Oliver began to get impatient. With nothing for the navy to do, Oliver had not minded loafing around home, but now that there was a war to be fought, and a naval war at that, he was anxious for action.

But no orders were forthcoming. For almost a year after war was declared Oliver haunted Newport in search of news. Robert Smith succeeded Benjamin Stoddert as Secretary of the Navy and Oliver immediately put in a bid for active duty.

"Maybe you'll have better luck with Smith," his father remarked. "I don't think Stoddert cared much for me."

Still no orders came, nor much news either. The *Enterprize* took a Tripolitan polacre in the Mediterranean, but had to let it go for want of authority. When a bigger navy blockades a smaller one, there isn't much chance for action.

So the summer dragged along. Commodore Silas Talbot resigned from the navy in September, making, as Oliver remarked, a wee bit more room at the top.

"There's always room at the top for a good man," his father replied, "but you'll never get there unless they give you a chance to show yourself."

Still Oliver was not alone. No one in the navy was making any headway. Even the four crews in the Mediterranean were getting little or no action. Finally Dale and Sterrett returned home in the

President and *Enterprize,* leaving the *Essex* and the *Philadelphia* to carry on the blockade of Tripoli.

Commodore Dale had a few words for the president's ear and the president promptly passed them along to Congress. The United States Navy was going to make no impression on the Bashaw of Tripoli unless it had the power to capture enemy ships. It took Congress a month to convince itself of these facts, but finally on February 6, 1802, eight months after war had been declared, Congress authorized the capture of Tripolitan ships.

On the strength of this a relief squadron was ordered to the Mediterranean, but the *Enterprize* was the only one ready to go. The *Chesapeake,* Thomas Truxton; the *Constellation,* James Murray; the *Adams,* Edward Preble; had to wait until they could be fitted out.

Oliver fretted and fretted. Here was a chance for action. Certainly he would be ordered to sea this time, but the *Enterprize* returned to the Mediterranean in February and the *Constellation* broke ground in March. Still Oliver rotted on the beach. Truxton resigned the same month and command of the *Chesapeake* as well as of the relief squadron was given to William V. Morris.

Then, when it seemed the navy had completely forgotten that he existed, came an order to report to Captain Preble of the U.S.S. *Adams* at New York City. The order was dated April 1st.

CHAPTER TWENTY

The "Adams"

"'ADAMS', EH?" MUTTERED CHRISTOPHER RAYMOND Perry as Oliver showed him his orders. "With Preble for a captain. Strict, he is. Puts everything down in black and white, though, so you know where you stand. Served as a lieutenant under Little in the Revolution. Spent some time in the prison ship *Jersey*, too."

Oliver smiled. "Seems though all our mariners of that era must have had a taste of the *Jersey*."

"All the ones with hair on their chests did," retorted Christopher Perry. "The ones who landed up in *Jersey*, the *Whitby*, the Sugar Warehouse in New York City or Dartmoor Prison in England were the ones who took chances. And it will be the same ones who either lick the Barbary pirates or find themselves as slaves on the Barbary Coast."

But the thought of slavery did not stay in Oliver's mind. It had been nearly two years since he had been on active duty. His appointment still seemed like a mirage, and he packed his chest automatically. He need have had no worry about his chest, for his mother, not to mention his three brothers and three sisters, were just falling all over themselves trying to be of help. At least all but Alexander, age ten months, were falling. He was being fallen over.

Oliver finally left for New York City after having waited impatiently for his new uniform to be made. He could scarcely squeeze into the old one. The trip from Newport was a pleasant one, for Oliver hadn't been on anything bigger than a sloop since he left the *General Greene*. Then, too, Long Island Sound was familiar water.

Once on Manhattan Island, Oliver reported to the yard where the *Adams* was being repaired. There he found that Captain Preble had been ill for nearly two weeks and that Charles Ludlow, son of the navy's New York agent, was acting as lieutenant and in charge of the ship.

"You can hang a hammock in the steerage for the present and get your meals at that house at the head of the wharf," young Ludlow told Oliver. "As for duties, I guess the only thing to be done is to watch the men and see that the work moves along rapidly. Most of the work has been done. The water's in and we should be moving out into the stream shortly."

While waiting for his chest to be brought aboard, Oliver examined his new home. She was much like the *General Greene,* although of smaller beam and greater depth.

"Good sailer," Ludlow informed him. "But she isn't too good as a frigate because her masts are so tall we have had to load her up with ballast, which leaves only enough room in her hold for three months' provisions and stores."

"She looks to be in good shape," Oliver said.

"Ought to be. About the only thing left of the original timber is her keelson. Why Captain Preble didn't build a new ship is beyond me. We've had her hoved, calked her, shod her keel, coppered her bottom, raised the spar deck four inches, and completely rebuilt her from wales to gunwales. We've put in new beams and planking on the gun deck besides replacing all of the running rigging, masts and spars."

Although most of the crew had been signed on there were few officers on hand, which left Oliver with little to do but wait for his superiors and their orders. While waiting he learned that all the government buildings at the yard had been sold and that all remaining timber had been moved across the East River to Wallabout Bay on Long Island where the government was building its new navy yard. It seemed more than a coincidence to Oliver that the government had picked the spot where the prison ships *Jersey* and *Whitby* had anchored as the site for its new navy yard.

Then things began to happen. Captain Preble resigned his command of the *Adams* because of ill-health and Captain Hugh Campbell was ordered to replace him. Campbell, Oliver recalled with mixed feelings, was the man who had replaced his father on the *General Greene*. But before Captain Campbell could reach the scene, Lieutenant Isaac Hull arrived and took command.

It was amazing how order appeared out of chaos as soon as Lieutenant Hull stepped on deck of the

Adams. That Oliver decided at once he liked this man was not surprising, for Oliver was somewhat prejudiced by the reports he had heard on Hull during the brush with the French in the West Indies. The successful cutting-out expedition that Hull performed at Puerto Plata was one thing that stood out in Oliver's memory. Another was the way in which Hull, sailing the *Constitution,* outmaneuvered a British frigate in a sunrise-to-sunset race for a cask of Madeira wine.

First thing Hull did, after being introduced to the officers, was to post the new Naval Regulations issued by President Jefferson, prescribing the duties of all officers. Oliver, being Oliver, first studied the duties of a midshipman and then at once studied the duties of the position which he hoped to fill soon, that of lieutenant.

The regulations gave midshipmen no particular assignment, other than to keep a journal which was to be turned over to the commanding officer at regular intervals. Aside from that, Oliver's job was to learn as much as possible about the business of being an officer. With Hull as his immediate superior, Oliver decided he would learn a lot.

One thing Oliver learned quickly was that, regardless of who was in command, frigates seldom sailed when they were supposed to. He also learned that naval officers were very jealous of their rank. No sooner had Hull arrived than he was informed of the resignation of Captain Preble. At once he assumed he would be given command of the ship and at once he was disappointed.

The appointment of Captain Campbell to the command of the *Adams* produced rumors that Hull was going to resign from the navy. Yet when Campbell arrived near the end of April, Hull was still in uniform and Campbell took over the task of trying to get the ship to sea.

Campbell found the powder on board defective. He also found that the workmen had not finished

WEIGHING ANCHOR

as he expected. In fact, his own cabin was not completed and he had to sleep on shore. In addition, no attention had been paid to the caliber of the guns when shot had been ordered and it all had to be replaced. Oliver was now in a position to appreciate better the troubles his father had had in getting the *General Greene* to sea. As days became weeks and weeks became months he became even more sympathetic.

Finally, on June 10th the *Adams* broke ground for her 3,000-mile trip to the Mediterranean.

For forty-one days the *Adams* traveled across the Atlantic and in that time Oliver learned to know his ship and shipmates well, almost too well, for in some instances familiarity had brought contempt. But to make up for these instances, Oliver had struck up a strong friendship with Lieutenant Hull and it was a lucky strike, for Hull knew his business and he was not averse to helping a young midshipman. With little work to be done Oliver had plenty of time to listen and learn.

Then on July 21, 1802, the *Adams* raised Tarifa, the southernmost tip of Spain. Oliver was on the quarter-deck with Hull when the cry "Land, ho!" came down from the masthead.

"That will be the Moorish Castle on Tarifa Island," Hull remarked, "and we'll make a point of keeping clear."

"Why, sir?" asked Oliver.

"The current in the middle of the Straits always runs due east. Toward either shore the current is apt to run toward the west. So now that we are headed for Gibraltar itself we'll stick to the middle of the Straits until we are abeam of the peninsula."

"Why should the current always run in an easterly direction?" asked Oliver.

"It's just one of those things. Why should the tide fall fifty and sixty feet in the Bay of Fundy?"

By this time Oliver could see land on either quarter. It was rugged country, Spain to port and Morocco to starboard. He was not surprised that the Straits were so narrow, for he had studied the ship's charts and discovered that only nine miles of water separated the two continents at one point.

The *Adams* was getting a chance to prove that she was a good sailer, for not only did she have the

current with her, but also the traditional east wind
of the Straits. As a result she had a sizable bone
in her teeth as she neared Gibraltar Bay. Long before the *Adams* reached the mouth of the bay Oliver
could see the towering rock on the peninsula that
formed the eastern shore of the bay.

Then Hull wore ship and brought the *Adams*
toward the foot of the rock. As the frigate drew
nearer Oliver could make out the town nestled
between the bay and the mountain. It was some
time before he could take his eyes off the famous
landmark, but when he did he quickly realized that
the *Adams* had considerable company. There were
four ships of the line at anchor, three frigates and
two brigs.

"Three English seventy-four's," Oliver heard
Captain Campbell remark as he swept the bay with
his glass. Then the captain's voice took on a slight
degree of excitement. "And there's the *Chesapeake!*
Looks like she's just dropped anchor herself. You
may prepare to return her salute, Mr. Hull."

The men needed no urging as they leapt to
their positions for the ceremony. None mentioned it,
but Oliver sensed a feeling that here was a chance
to show the British that the United States Navy was
shipshape in the matter of traditions and customs
as well as the matter of fighting.

CHAPTER TWENTY-ONE

Promotion

THAT NIGHT THE CREWS OF THE *Adams* AND *Chesapeake* exchanged visits and over their rum they exchanged news.

What was the news from home? The Secretary of the Navy had asked that rations be increased; Lieutenant David Porter was said to have killed a man in a brawl at Fell's Point; the government had laid down keels for some light cruisers for use on the Barbary Coast.

What was the news in the Mediterranean? Morocco had declared war on the United States, but the American consul was still hoping to make a settlement; the *Chesapeake* had seen no action in the two months it had been on the station. In fact, the *Chesapeake* had seen no pirates, which was apparently as the pirates would have it. Their little polacres were no match for a frigate and they knew it. Hence, all there was to be done was to sail back and forth from Gibraltar to Alexandria with any American vessels that wanted to be escorted. There was no danger of attack. In fact, there would be no trouble at all if there were enough frigates available to escort all the merchantmen.

What about cleaning out the pirate ships? Perhaps—when the government's new light cruisers were launched. Now all the pirates did was run under their forts or in close to the reefy shore whenever they saw a frigate. It was just like trying to catch a school of minnows with your hands.

Oliver pondered over the last remark. Trying to catch minnows with your hands. That was the

CORSAIR

way it had been in the West Indies with the French. He wondered if he ever would get to see real action.

Hence the next morning when Oliver learned that the *Adams* had been ordered to stay at Gibraltar to keep the Tripolitan frigate *Meshouda* from getting to sea, he was not as disappointed as he might have been. Nevertheless, he expressed his feelings to Hull at the first opportunity.

The lieutenant smiled. "I feel the same way

about it as you do," he said, "but in your case the lack of action is to be desired. You still have a lot to learn about handling a crew and handling a ship. The longer you wait the better prepared you will be when action comes."

If anyone else had said that to Oliver he probably would have shrugged it off as good, yet dull advice, but Hull—well, Hull was Hull. So Oliver immediately settled down to make the most of any experience he could get while on the station.

Blockading the *Meshouda* was not going to provide much experience, Oliver could see, but being in Gibraltar Bay was good training for any midshipman, and most lieutenants too for that matter.

"Watch those British frigates," Hull advised Oliver. "The British have been in this business a long time and they do things shipshape. We might be able to teach them a thing or two about fighting, but they know their discipline, which is half the battle. With their discipline and our men we'd need not be afraid of anyone.

"The only trouble with their system is that they are too severe with their men. That's why they have so many deserters. On the other hand, British officers have to be severe. With so many ships to fill the government has to take every man it can get and most of the ones it gets are not so good."

The first thing Oliver noticed about the British was that all their ships sounded only one bell at 6:30 of the dog watch whereas all the other ships in the bay sounded five bells. That required an explanation and Hull was the man to give it.

"There's a story around," Hull said, "that back in seventeen-ninety-seven some British seamen planned to mutiny. The uprising was to come at five bells of the dog watch, but the ship's officers learned of the plan and so when six-thirty came they had only one bell sounded instead of five. Ever since, British ships sound only one bell instead of five."

And Oliver learned to tell a ship's nationality by the cut of her jib. Spanish ships carried very small ones or none at all. French ships usually carried two while the British carried but one. He also learned that ships were painted red inboard so that spilled blood would be less noticeable. He learned too that the men didn't mind tarring the standing rigging because the tar made their trousers waterproof. He learned that a Spanish ship was called His Most Catholic Majesty's ship and that a Portuguese ship was called His Most Faithful Majesty's ship; that messmate came before shipmate, shipmate before stranger, and stranger before a dog; that seamen were likely to tamper with the ship's glass to make their watches go more quickly.

But the one thing he wanted to learn most, how to handle a ship in battle, was not forthcoming. The *Adams* tried to find a fight in the direction of Morocco, where the emperor was using strong language, but instead of subduing that pirate the *Adams* in company with the *Chesapeake* and the *Enterprize* simply scared the emperor into making peace with the United States again. The ships merely crossed the Straits of Gibraltar and appeared before the walled city of Tangier while the American consul was in conference with the emperor. That settled that question. Now the problem was to convince Tripoli that the United States Navy was in earnest.

However, the Bashaw of Tripoli was not a man to be brought to terms by a mere show of force. Nor was he one to shudder at such indirect methods as blockading. Without authority to take more drastic steps there was little the U.S. fleet could do in that direction. Hence, July became August and August rapidly approached September. In fact, there was only six days left in the month when Oliver was summoned before Captain Campbell.

As he was admitted to the captain's cabin, Oliver found that Lieutenant Hull also was present.

"Mr. Perry," the captain began, "it is my pleasure to inform you that from this day forth you will consider yourself as an acting lieutenant." Captain Campbell paused to let his message sink in. "You understand that you will not be allowed to wear an epaulet until you have received your commission from the Secretary of the Navy."

Only out of force of habit was Oliver able to make a reply.

There was a slight pause. Captain Campbell cleared his throat.

"As a matter of fact," he said, "it was Lieutenant Hull's suggestion that I inform you of your provisional promotion on your birthday."

Oliver looked toward his friend and smiled.

"Yes," said Hull, "because I became a lieutenant on my birthday too, only it was my twentyfifth birthday and not my seventeenth as in your case."

GUN DECK OF A FRIGATE

CHAPTER TWENTY-TWO

Action

ALL WINTER LONG THE *Adams* WAS STATIONED AT Gibraltar and all winter long the morale of its crew weakened. For a while the novelty of being an acting lieutenant kept up Oliver's spirits, but gradually he found himself becoming irritable like the others.

"Talk, talk, talk," officers and men grumbled. "If Congress wants this business settled why doesn't it let the navy do its job? What's the navy for? To carry diplomats or to fight?"

There was no answer to these questions. Orders were orders, and the order said Morocco was to be blockaded. Even when a settlement was finally made with the emperor the crew of the *Adams* was not satisfied.

"Now we'll go blockade some other port," they said, "and leave the Emperor of Morocco to do as he pleases."

That was just what happened. In April the *Adams* was ordered to join the rest of the fleet at Malta. Pressure was to be brought on Tripoli to the south.

Oliver enjoyed the trip up the Mediterranean, for the *Adams,* escorting a convoy, was forced to visit most of the important cities on the northern coast. To a native of flat, drab Rhode Island the colorful and mountainous coast line was fascinating.

At Malta the *Adams* found the frigates *New York* and *John Adams* and the schooner *Enterprize* awaiting her, and there Oliver learned of the plan of action. He gathered his information in the wardroom of the *New York* from Lieutenant David Porter of the *New York* and Lieutenant James Lawrence of the *Enterprize*.

"The commodore is going to try to scare the bashaw into coming to terms," Porter said. "The idea is to sail the squadron back and forth in front of Tripoli and then go ashore and see if the bashaw's knees are shaking."

"I don't see the point," Lawrence remarked. "Supposing we do make him come to terms. How do we know he'll keep his word? None of these pirates ever have."

Oliver spoke up.

"If I had any say in the matter, we'd settle this business once and for all now. For one reason, I've been looking for action for four years; for another reason, if we don't get tough we'll spend the rest of our lives sailing around the Mediterranean."

But despite the opinions of the younger officers, their orders were to proceed to the coast of Tripoli and that is what they did, although not together. The *Adams* was delayed at Malta in stocking and watering and was several days late in reaching Tripoli. She arrived in time to learn that the *New York*, the *John Adams* and the *Enterprize* had discovered a convoy of eleven merchantmen, but although they had driven the enemy ships ashore they had failed in an attempt to burn them.

Now Commodore Morris was planning to attack the three gunboats of the convoy that had escaped into Tripoli. The *John Adams* was ordered into the van and it was almost a fatal move, for as the *Adams* fell off and brought her starboard guns into play, she found herself on the weather beam of the former and promptly cut away the foretop gallant bowlines on her first and only volley. With no wind the *Adams* was unable to better her position and was forced to lie back and watch. Meanwhile the *New York* found herself in a similar position and the enemy gunboats easily escaped under the city's batteries.

Back in the wardroom, the young officers continued their lament.

"It's foolish to try to catch a gunboat with a frigate in these tricky waters. What we need is a few small boats of our own," Lawrence said.

"The only chance we've got is to catch one of these fellows in the open sea," added Porter.

"And don't forget," Oliver inserted, "unless there is a good stiff breeze, these gunboats will out-maneuver these frigates."

For once Commodore Morris seemed to be in agreement. And the next day he ordered the *Adams* to the westward of Tripoli, the *John Adams* to the eastward and kept the *New York* and the *Enterprize* to the north of the city in the hope of catching three gunboats which were reported at large.

Captain Campbell had scarcely set his course when the masthead spotted a sail to the westward. The sail turned out to be not one, but two, and as the *Adams* bore down under partially filled sails, the number increased to ten. So intent was Oliver on the chase that he did not notice that the *Enterprize* had entered into the action. Being a lightweight ship and using her sweeps, the *Enterprize* was able to outdistance the *Adams* and make first contact with the enemy.

"Looks like another load of wheat to me," muttered Captain Campbell, as though he were explaining away the fact that the *Enterprize* had beaten him to action.

As the two American warships approached the small merchantmen, Oliver could readily see that they were quickly taking shelter in a small bay and that the *Adams* would have to be content to fire on them from a rather long range. But tame as the promised action appeared, it was the first that the *Adams* had undertaken in the ten months she had been in the Mediterranean.

It was five o'clock in the afternoon when Captain Campbell gave the order to fire and the results were immediate. Boats from four of the ships were put over and rapidly headed toward the *Adams*. Captain Campbell gave the order to cease fire and made ready to receive his visitors. They all came aboard jabbering profusely; when they had been calmed down, it was learned that they were Tunisians.

"Tunisians or Tripolitans," Captain Campbell

replied, "if your boats are not alongside of us by midnight, I'll burn every one of them."

With these definite terms well impressed upon them, the Tunisians scampered back to their boats and returned to their commands.

Meanwhile, a crowd had been gathering on shore and to keep themselves amused, the crew of

SHIP'S LONG GUN (BELOW DECKS)

the *Adams* tested their guns now and then. By night-fall the rest of the squadron was on the scene.

At dark, three boats under the command of Lieutenant David Porter reconnoitered toward the shore, but were fired upon before accomplishing their mission. The rest of the night was without event, and in the morning preparations were made for burning the merchantmen. Seven boats, three from the *Adams*, Lieutenant Ludlow, two from the *New York,* Lieutenant Porter, and two from the *Enterprize,* Lieutenant Lawrence, advanced on the merchantmen. Once again Oliver was forced to watch the action. The fire boats succeeded in igniting the merchantmen and once again the Tripolitans, despite the barrage from the frigates, came from behind their breastworks and extinguished the craft.

Anxious as he was for action, Oliver had to admit that the ineffective barrage of the *Adams* soon turned into a sporting proposition with the gun crews vying with each other to see which could come the closest to the moving figures on the beach.

Once again the Americans had failed for want of gunboats, and once again they had failed to impress the bashaw. After a week of negotiations Commodore Morris ordered Captain John Rodgers to blockade the harbor of Tripoli with the *Adams, John Adams,* and *Enterprize* while he sailed with the *New York* for Malta.

No sooner had the three ships taken their stations off Tripoli than the *Enterprize* spotted the bashaw's largest cruiser off the beach. Then occurred the one successful offensive of the voyage. For forty-five minutes the *John Adams* and the *Enterprize* poured broadsides into the *Tripolitan.* Having silenced her guns the American ships were rewarded by seeing her suddenly blow up.

The *Adams* meanwhile was casually patrolling to the west of the city.

Four months later when Commodore Morris was ordered to turn his command over to Captain Rodgers, Oliver thought it very fitting that the unfortunate *Adams* should be the one to carry the equally unlucky Morris home.

CHAPTER TWENTY-THREE

The Wrong Place Again

ACTING LIEUTENANT OLIVER HAZARD PERRY MADE quite an impression on the friends he had left behind in Newport. His eighteen months at sea had changed him. His face was still round, but his leathery tan gave it an appearance of age. But despite the impression he knew he made, Perry realized he was not the man he might have been had he been given the opportunity. Yet you couldn't tell your friends that, especially when you were a tall, good-looking young officer. Porter and Lawrence had been given opportunities and Porter had been wounded twice. Both lieutenants had been retained with the squadron. Perry couldn't decide whether it was he that was unlucky or the *Adams*.

No sooner had Perry landed home than reports came back from the Mediterranean to substantiate his feelings. Commodore Preble, who commanded the relief squadron, was wasting no time. He had proceeded to Tripoli only to learn that the *Philadelphia*, Captain William Bainbridge, had been captured when she went aground while chasing a Tripolitan ship. The officers and crew, including Perry's friend, Lieutenant Porter, had been taken prisoner. Preble thereupon established a blockade of Tripoli, for the winter gales were coming up and there was little else he could do.

To make Perry even more restless, another friend, Lieutenant Stephen Decatur, Jr., became a national hero by destroying the *Philadelphia,* which the Tripolitans had captured and repaired. Disguising his ketch *Intrepid,* Decatur had sailed boldly into the harbor of Tripoli and, despite being surrounded by enemy ships and shore batteries, had boarded the *Philadelphia,* set her afire and escaped without losing a man.

"One of the most daring naval maneuvers ever undertaken," was the way Lord Nelson of the British Navy had put it when the news reached him at Toulon, where he was blockading the French fleet.

That Lieutenant Lawrence also had taken part in the expedition made Perry feel that he too might have had a hand in it had he been on the scene. He tried to think how he would have acted had he been Decatur or Lawrence.

But despite the exciting news from the Mediterranean, Perry could not spend all his time wishing he were in the thick of the action. He had some studying to do for the examination for his lieutenant's commission. It was to be an oral one and his success would depend as much on the speed with which he answered questions as on his knowledge. Yet the examination never came and finally he applied for active duty.

Four frigates were to be sent to the Mediterranean, the *President, Congress, Constellation,* and *Essex.* Perry waited. First, he thought he would like to be attached to the *Constellation*. Then he thought he would prefer the *President*. Finally, after weeks of waiting, he decided he didn't care on which he shipped just so long as it was one of the four. He began to wonder if his bad luck would ever leave him.

It did, suddenly. His orders arrived, addressed to Midshipman Oliver H. Perry.

> Navy Dept. April 23, 1804
>
> You will consider yourself attached to the Frigate The Constellation as one of her Officers and will immediately report yourself to her Commanding Officer.
>
> (Signed)   Robert Smith

"Captain Campbell," Perry said out loud as he read his orders. "He must have asked to have me sail with him."

Being eighteen years old, in the pink of condition and anxious to get back to sea, Perry didn't mind the torturous stagecoach trip to the new capital at Washington, D.C. It mattered little to him that he had to travel sixteen and eighteen hours a day. Nor was he disappointed on his arrival to find nothing but mud holes and a few unfinished buildings. He was interested only in knowing when he was to receive his commission and when the *Constellation* was to sail.

"Don't worry about your commission," Captain Campbell advised him. "You are to be my second lieutenant and that's all that matters at the present. The experience will be just as valuable, epaulet or no epaulet. As for the *Constellation,* I hope to break ground before July."

But Oliver did worry about his commission. He'd been a midshipman long enough. He was tired of running errands for the other officers and he wanted some responsibility of his own.

"But now I won't have a chance to take my examination," Perry said. "There won't be time before we sail."

"I'm not so sure about that," replied Captain Campbell. "You know as well as I do it takes a long time to ready a ship for sea."

"I also know it takes a long time for the Navy Department to issue orders," Perry continued.

Captain Campbell placed his hand on the young officer's shoulder.

"You just do your job as well as you have done it to date and we'll worry about the commission."

That ended the conversation, but it did not settle Perry's mind. Just because your captain knew you were qualified to be a lieutenant didn't mean that anyone else knew. Had anyone watched him for the next two weeks, however, they would have been thoroughly convinced that Perry knew his business. He helped supervise the loading of barrels and barrels of supplies—"harness casks," some of the older men called the barrels that held the salted beef. They swore that the meat in them had been tanned before brining.

There were other things that had to be watched, too—the placing of the ballast, the repairs of the ship. Perry had his hand in all of these. And within two weeks he could have told you the size and kind of every piece of wood in the *Constellation*.

Then one morning in early June, Captain Campbell called him to his cabin.

"I've received word from Commodore Barron that he has received your commission from the Secretary of the Navy. You are to apply to him to be examined and if he finds you to be qualified, he will give you your commission. I suggest you apply right away, for I am sure you can pass the examination."

Perry was sure, too, and at once he addressed an application to Commodore Barron at Hampton, Virginia. Then began a race with time, to see which would come first, the orders to sail or the orders to appear at Hampton for his examination.

The orders to sail came first.

CHAPTER TWENTY-FOUR

Closing the Barn Door

IT WAS 4:30 A.M. ON THE MORNING OF JULY 3, 1804, when signal number 1205 was broken out on the commodore's flagship, the frigate *President*, in Hampton Roads. The order to break ground was answered by Captain John Rodgers of the *Congress*, Captain James Barron of the *Essex*, and Captain Campbell of the *Constellation*. An hour later the four frigates made sail in light airs.

This was the squadron that was to reinforce the six U.S. ships now under Commodore Preble's command in the Mediterranean.

This was the squadron that was expected to bring about the fall of Tripoli, for together with the ships already on the scene this would be the largest force ever assembled by the United States Navy. Besides the frigate *Constitution*, Preble's flagship, there now were stationed in the Mediterranean the brig *Argus*, Master Commandant Isaac Hull, the brig *Siren*, Master Commandant Charles Stewart, the schooner *Vixen*, Master Commandant John Smith, the schooner *Nautilus*, Lieutenant Richard Somers, and the schooner *Enterprize* under Perry's friend Stephen Decatur, who was now a captain. The frigate *John Adams*, which had been found to be a slow sailer, had left Hampton Roads a week earlier, but was to be used only as a transport. It was under the command of Master Commandant Isaac Chauncey.

Tripoli, which presumably would fall once this battery of 152 extra guns was leveled against it, was still a good three thousand miles away when the squadron came to anchor that night off Old Point Comfort. Light airs continued the next day and at ten o'clock in the morning the squadron was becalmed off Cape Henry. From then on, however, it was a case of making and shortening sail in order to keep the squadron together.

Eight days out from Cape Henry came a cry from the masthead.

"Ahoy the quarter-deck!"

Perry, who was the officer of the watch, stepped forward and glanced aloft.

"The *Congress* seems to be coming about, sir," the seaman called down.

"What do you make to be her trouble?" asked Perry.

"Hard to say, sir, she's in irons," replied the seaman.

"What's her position?" yelled Perry.

"About three points on the port bow, sir," replied the seaman.

Perry turned quickly and ordered the helmsman to change his course. Perry reached for his megaphone and kept his eye to port waiting for a glimpse of the *Congress*'s topsails. Soon they appeared on the horizon and after what seemed to

Perry an interminable time the *Constellation* was in a position to hail. By this time it was definitely established that the *Congress* had lost a man overboard, for her stern cutter could be seen searching the surrounding waters. The hail produced the information that three maintopmen had fallen overboard while trying to reef topsails and that three others had fallen to the deck, two of them dying immediately. Meanwhile the *President* and *Essex* had come on the scene, but after finding they could be of no assistance resumed their courses.

The rest of the voyage was without incident, although there was little time for relaxing since the job of beating against head winds and keeping the squadron together was one which called for continual working of the sails. After three weeks of buffeting Commodore Barron finally signaled to the ships to break the formation and make their separate ways as best they could to Gibraltar. This proved a test for the seamanship of the crews and the sailing qualities of the frigates and as a result the *Congress* was the first to arrive in Gibraltar Bay, although the *Constellation* managed to keep her in sight for the last five days of the trip. For Perry as well as the rest of the crew, it was a relief to see the headlands of Spain once again after thirty-eight days at sea. Soon afterward the *President* dropped anchor in the bay. It was not until half past eleven the next morning that the *Essex* appeared.

The squadron immediately began laying in stores and water and the ships' companies took the opportunity to attend to their long-neglected washing. Three days later the *President* and *Constellation* were ordered to Tripoli and the *Congress* and *Essex* to Morocco.

The reports from Tripoli were that Commodore Preble was carrying on an active campaign in an effort to blast the emperor into submission. But much as the *President* and the *Constellation* would like to have made a speedy trip aloft, they were balked by light airs and calms. Seven days after they left Gibraltar they had only reached Cape de Gata on the southern coast of Spain and there they were once again becalmed.

Commodore Barron took the opportunity to invite Captain Campbell to dinner. It was not to be as pleasant as he expected, for at seven bells in the afternoon watch the *Constellation,* which had a slight way on, was shaken as though she had grazed her keel on a rock. There was no beat to quarters needed, for all hands ran on deck expecting to see the ship hard aground. The officer of the deck was bewildered and continually prodded the leadsman in the chains as to his soundings.

"I can't understand it," he said, as the officers gathered on the quarter-deck. "There seem to be no shoals or rocks anywhere around."

Then gathering himself together he ordered the ship about and prepared to hail Captain Campbell on board the *President.* As Perry looked in the direction of the flagship, he noticed that its crew was on deck too. On hailing the *President* it was learned that that ship had had a similar experience at precisely the same time as the *Constellation.* The *Presi-*

dent then bore down on a Spanish merchantman which was near by and returned with the startling information that the shock felt by all three ships had not been shoals but an earthquake, so that when the *Constellation* underwent a similar experience an hour and a half later there was no cause for alarm.

Twelve days later the *President* and *Constellation* arrived at Malta where they replenished their supplies as quickly as possible and shaped their courses south for Tripoli. It was September 9th when the two frigates joined the *Constitution* and the *Argus* only to learn that they were too late. Disaster had overtaken the American efforts to subdue the town. Perry learned the details from Master Commandant Hull when he went aboard the *Argus* that evening.

"You see," said Hull, "the idea was to send this infernal into the inner harbor under the walls of the bashaw's castle and to settle the matter with one terrific blast. Lieutenant Somers suggested the idea and Commodore Preble ordered him to prepare the *Intrepid,* the same boat that Decatur used when he burned the *Philadelphia*. Somers first placed fifteen thousand pounds of powder loosely in the hold of the ketch and on top of this two hundred and fifty thirteen-inch fuse shells with a train attached from the cabin and the forepeak.

"He took with him Lieutenant Henry Wadsworth from the brig *Scourge* and four volunteer seamen from his own ship, the *Nautilus*. On the night of the second and third, he tried to move the

Intrepid but was unsuccessful, due to light winds. On the third night Somers felt that the enemy was suspicious and told his crew that no man need accompany him who had not come to the resolution to blow himself up rather than be captured, for Somers felt that the Tripolitans were running low on powder and would try to capture the *Intrepid*.

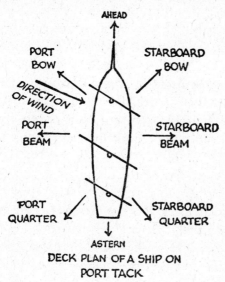

DECK PLAN OF A SHIP ON
PORT TACK

"Every man jack of them no sooner had heard Somers's speech than he stepped up and asked that he might be permitted to apply the match. It was a pretty exciting time, I can tell you, and every one of those men knew that he was doomed, but they joked about willing their old clothes to their messmates as they cast off.

"It was about two bells of the night watch when

the *Intrepid* started. She was followed by the *Nautilus*, which was ordered to pick up the crew of the *Intrepid* in case they should succeed. Somers must have been right in his supposition that the Tripolitans were suspicious, for the *Intrepid* never reached her destination.

"We heard two alarm guns from the shore batteries and a few minutes later the *Intrepid* blew up with as terrible an explosion as I ever want to hear. Some of the shells burst nearly three hundred feet in the air. The *Nautilus* stayed inshore till broad daylight, but there wasn't even a spar or a plank left of the *Intrepid*. We learned later that Midshipman Joseph Israel had been sent with orders from Commodore Preble to Somers and had remained on the *Intrepid*."

Perry stared into his glass. There seemed nothing for him to say.

"I am afraid it's taken the wind out of our sails," Hull continued. "Before this happened it looked as though we might, with a little help, beat the bashaw into submission. We had made five attacks on the town in the last month and had done considerable damage. Somers was right in thinking that the Tripolitans were running short of gunpowder. Had the *President* and *Constellation* arrived sooner, Preble might not have been tempted to take Somers's suggestion of sending an infernal into the harbor."

The death of Somers and his crew had taken the wind out of the American sails, and before Commodore Barron could reorganize his forces, he de-

cided to withhold any further attacks on the town
and prepare his squadron to go into winter quarters.

Once again Perry found himself blockading the
port of Tripoli.

"It always seems," he confided to Hull, "that I
have to close the barn door after the horse has been
stolen."

BRIG

CHAPTER TWENTY-FIVE

Peace with Tripoli

AS USUAL THE SCUTTLEBUTT PROVIDED THE DETAILS of further plans to subdue Tripoli. A joint attack on Derna was to be made in the spring. William Eaton, former United States consul to Tunis, would go to Alexandria and make plans there with the ex-Pasha of Tripoli for land operations. An army would be formed and marched six hundred miles across the desert. At the appointed time the *Argus, Hornet,* and *Nautilus* would attack Derna from the sea while Eaton and his army attacked from the land.

True, the scuttlebutt was not absolutely accurate, but the rumors emanating from around the water supply produced the general idea of what was to come. And that is precisely what happened. In April, 1805, Derna fell and Commodore Barron had another lever in his negotiations for peace.

But Commodore Barron was not to get the satisfaction of seeing the negotiations completed, for early in May he became ill and was forced to turn the command of the squadron over to Captain John Rodgers. The shift in personnel had its reverbations all the way down the chain of command.

"Captain Campbell wishes to see you, sir," Perry was told one evening in May as the *Constellation* cruised off the harbor of Tripoli.

Perry acknowledged the order and immediately proceeded below. His knock was answered by a quiet "Come in."

Perry opened the door and entered the stuffy cabin.

"Sit down, lieutenant," said Captain Campbell, rising to offer a glass of wine. "I have good news for you and bad news for me."

Perry waited expectantly as Captain Campbell filled his glass.

"The return of Commodore Barron to the States leaves some vacancies in the fleet and I have been asked to recommend a junior officer to serve with Master Commandant Dent on the schooner *Nautilus*. Much against my wishes I have recommended you. For while I would prefer to have you continue under my command, I realize that I must think of your future. There are several reasons why it is to your advantage to serve on the *Nautilus*. In the first place, it is much better to be a big frog in a small puddle than a small frog in a big puddle. In addition, your first command undoubtedly will be a smaller vessel and it will be well for you to be prepared to accept such a command."

"Yes, sir," Perry said. "I appreciate the opportunity. Thank you."

"Don't thank me. The navy needs officers, good officers, and I think you deserve to be moved along as rapidly as possible." Captain Campbell paused. Then, lifting his glass toward his lieutenant, he said, "Here's luck."

Two days later Perry was piped aboard the

Nautilus. He retired immediately to his quarters and prepared to arrange his belongings.

"Somers's old ship," he said to himself. "Fourteen guns and a hundred seventy tons. Well, she may be one of the smallest ships in the squadron, but there's nothing to prevent her from being one of the best."

While the young officer adjusted himself to his new assignment the peace negotiations continued in the pasha's palace, with the result that on June 10th, a salute of twenty-one guns resounded from the shore batteries to be answered by the *Constitution.* The United States were at peace with Tripoli. To swing the deal a ransom of $60,000 had been given for the release of the crew of the *Philadelphia.*

No sooner had the Tripolitan business been cleared up than the Bey of Tunis began muttering in his beard. He continued to mutter until Commodore Rodgers appeared off the harbor with his squadron. The sight of the United States ships together with some words of advice from Rodgers settled that little matter.

For three months Perry served under Dent on the *Nautilus,* which for the most part was used as a dispatch boat. Then came the rumor that Dent was to be transferred. Who would succeed him? At the mess table the lieutenants spoke cynically of the probability of the command being given to some outsider, but secretly each felt himself qualified and deserving of the command, and each tried a little harder to make an impression. It was in vain, for in

August Lieutenant Samuel Evans took command of the *Nautilus*.

There was not much for the *Nautilus* to do, despite the considerable amount of activity going on about her. The Spanish and French fleets were maneuvering off Cadiz, Spain, indicating trouble for the British. Tension built up rapidly until October when the British fleet under Lord Nelson met and defeated this mighty armada. Yet the British victory at Trafalgar was not complete, for the brilliant Lord Nelson had been killed. A week after the battle, when Nelson's body, preserved in brandy, was brought to Gibraltar, the *Nautilus* was there to witness the ceremony.

Two months later Perry was detached from the *Nautilus* and ordered to the *Constitution*, Commodore Rodgers's flagship.

But flagship or not, the *Constitution* proved just another frigate and another study in routine for Perry.

"Different ships, different long splices," was the way the maintopmen put it, but to the young Rhode Islander it was: "Different ships, different blockades."

The *Constitution* stayed in the Mediterranean for almost a year and during that time it did little but convoy, cruise, and catch rumors.

Then the acting lieutenant was ordered aboard the *Essex* for the trip home. The trouble with the Barbary pirates had been settled temporarily. Meanwhile other naval troubles had arisen. British and French men-of-war were seizing American merchant-men.

CHAPTER TWENTY-SIX

Officer Ashore

BEING FREE, WHITE AND TWENTY-ONE, AS WELL AS A good-looking naval officer, Perry acted accordingly when he arrived home in Newport in October, 1806. No party was too small for him to attend and there was no dearth of parties. Perry had to make up for the months he had spent in the Mediterranean.

Yet for all his gaiety it took him four months to meet Elizabeth Champlin Mason. Of course she was only sixteen years old which would explain why he hadn't met her on his last shore leave, but she was the daughter of a leading physician and a very pretty one at that. He thought he knew everyone of consequence in the town, but at a subscription dance early in the new year he made a shocking discovery. There was one person of considerable consequence he had not met.

Perry was standing near the entrance of the Masonic Hall when a young lady and her escort accompanied by two older women entered the room. The group obviously was not trying to make an impression by being late. It just so happened that there were only two public conveyances in the town and someone had to be last. Perry automatically glanced in the young lady's direction and she in his. Their

eyes met. Something clicked and the next thing Perry
knew a quivering sensation was running up and
down his spine. He watched the group as they
hesitantly sought the refuge of friends and he continued to watch the young lady as she and her escort
waited for a minuet to be completed. As though she

felt Perry's eyes upon her, the young lady looked
again in his direction. Again something clicked, but
this time, instead of leaving him nonplused, it
aroused his curiosity. He began asking questions—
subtly, of course. Who was this girl in the low-cut
green dress and white scarf? He thought he knew
everyone in the town.

Perry wasn't subtle enough to fool the friend

who answered his question, but he did find out what he wanted to know.

Thereafter things went along the way they usually do with a handsome officer of twenty-one and a pretty young lady of sixteen. Glances became dances and dances became invitations. It was a wonderful way to spend a shore leave, and as winter changed to spring and spring changed to summer Perry thought it was even more wonderful. He began to feel that civilian life was just as important to him as navy life, but he was wrong.

The first thing to bring a doubt to his mind was the arrival of his lieutenant's commission late in April. For five years he had waited for this official document, this piece of paper which would allow him to show the public at large he was a qualified lieutenant. There was another thing this piece of paper would do, however. It would give him a definite place in the line of younger officers awaiting commands. Of the five years he had been an acting lieutenant one had been spent on shore and the rest on the monotonous work in the Mediterranean. Now perhaps he would be considered for more important things. After all, he was sixth in seniority among the lieutenants of the United States Navy. Lest Washington should forget, he wrote, requesting active service.

The thing that really changed his mind about civilian life was the news from Hampton Roads in June that the U.S. frigate *Chesapeake,* Captain James Barron, had been attacked by the British vessel *Leopard.*

"This means war," said Perry when he heard of
the disaster and, despite her attractiveness, Elizabeth
Champlin Mason promptly vanished from his
thoughts.

"They've been itching for this for a long time,"
the young officer stated, as the *Chesapeake* affair was
hashed over in the shipping offices along Thames
Street. "They've been taking seamen off our merchant ships for a long time when they weren't taking the ships themselves. The French are no better.
It's a wonder we haven't declared war on both countries. Now the British have gone so far as to take
seamen from a United States frigate. I tell you the
navy won't stand for that sort of thing."

"Maybe not," added a bystander, "but three
men were killed and eighteen wounded and the
Chesapeake didn't answer with one shot. Doesn't
seem to me the navy can do much about stopping
the British if it isn't better prepared than that."

Perry's temper got the better of him.

"That statement calls for one of two things—
an apology or a duel," he said through clenched
teeth.

The bystander was quick to make peace.

"Now, now, lieutenant, I didn't mean to rub
you the wrong way. I'm not criticizing the navy.
It does a good job with what they give it to work
with. That's just the point I'm making. I don't think
we're prepared to fight the British."

"Preparation is beside the point," said Perry.
"The fact of the matter is that a United States frigate
has been blasted without cause. American seamen

have been killed by enemy action. We're not going to stand around and do nothing about it."

But Perry and the rest of the personnel of the United States Navy were forced to do just that. Congress wouldn't let them do otherwise.

Fortunately for Perry, his pleas for active duty were finally answered. He was ordered to New York to take charge of a flotilla of gunboats. It would have been hard for him to stay in Newport which, like all other coastal New England communities, depended upon the sea. With commerce interrupted, a feeling of resentment had arisen. New England merchants were demanding that something be done.

It was. In December Congress passed an Embargo Act, forbidding United States ships to leave for foreign ports and the navy was given the unpleasant job of seeing to it that the law was enforced. To order the ambitious young navy to turn to passive resistance and hold stubborn New Englanders in port was asking too much. The men who risked their fortunes on the high seas were not to be stopped completely. United States merchant ships still put to sea and still were captured by the British and French. Jefferson and his crowd could do as they pleased in Washington, but New England wasn't going to give up its bread and butter. It would secede from the Union first.

Meanwhile in February, 1808, Perry was ordered to Westerly to supervise the construction of gunboats at that town as well as the Connecticut ports of Mystic and Norwich. It was distasteful work. In the first place, it meant that the government was still thinking in terms of defense. The money it was pouring into gunboats could have been put to far better use in frigates. Gunboats had been all right for use against the Barbary pirates, but if the United States were to go to war with England they would need frigates and plenty of them. In the second place, the assignment to Westerly meant that Perry's chances for real action were limited. But he took his orders without a word, for he had long since come to learn that it was the duty of naval officers to obey orders, not to question them. The United States Navy knew best.

For a little more than a year Perry was stationed in Westerly and almost all the time he was there he begged for more active service. Finally, he was ordered to take command of the schooner *Revenge* in Commodore Rodgers's squadron. And as though it were not exciting enough to receive his first command, he was given Newport as his station.

CHAPTER TWENTY-SEVEN

In Command

IT WAS APRIL, 1809, WHEN PERRY AT TWENTY-THREE took command of the *Revenge,* exactly ten years after he had joined the navy as a midshipman.

Things had changed considerably in those years, Perry thought as he watched his tailor shift his gold epaulet from his left shoulder to his right. No longer was he a subordinate; now he was a full-fledged officer with a heavy responsibility. His years at sea had matured him. He was the senior officer in the Perry household now, for his father had retired from the sea and had been made collector for the port of Newport. His two younger brothers, Raymond and Matthew, were just beginning their apprenticeship as midshipmen.

Other things had changed too. Commodore Preble was dead. The Embargo Act had been repealed. James Madison, who favored war with England, had been President of the United States for a month. Paul Hamilton had succeeded Robert Smith as Secretary of the Navy. Captain James Barron had been suspended for five years from the navy for his failure to offer resistance in the *Chesapeake-Leopard* affair. Robert Fulton had successfully navigated his steamboat, the *Clermont,* up the Hudson River from New York to Albany.

Perry was an experienced officer and the sensation he felt in taking command of the *Revenge* was not lack of confidence. That he could handle the ship he had not a doubt; that he could handle the men he did not doubt, either, for he had had little trouble with his subordinates up to now.

The crew of the *Revenge* was quick to learn that their new commander knew his business. From Campbell and Hull and Rodgers the lieutenant had absorbed much and his training showed in his new position. His courage and his even disposition he had inherited, but his seamanship and his passion for tempered discipline had come from his former superior officers. The crew of the *Revenge* did not realize all this, but it did realize that here was a man who had a mind of his own, an officer who wanted discipline, not for the sake of discipline but for the sake of efficiency. Exercising the guns was not so much of a chore under those conditions.

Perry had a whole year to train his crew, for he spent the summer in northern waters and the winter farther south, without incident. In April, 1810, he put into the Washington Navy Yard for repairs.

When the *Revenge* put to sea again, a month later, Midshipman Matthew Calbraith Perry was a member of her crew and Lieutenant Oliver Hazard Perry was quick to point out the difference between shipboard and fireside, just as his father had.

"Anywhere but home, it's 'sir' and 'Mr. Perry,'" Oliver told his brother, "and when I say 'jump' I mean jump, but I want you to understand that I am not trying to rub in my authority. In order to maintain discipline on this ship I must play no favorites. To me you must be just another member of the crew. Do I make myself clear?"

"Yes, sir," replied Matthew.

Then, with new orders to consider, the commander forgot his younger brother. The *Revenge* was to cruise off Charleston as protection for American merchantmen in that vicinity. For two months nothing of moment happened. Then one day in July a United States marshal came aboard. Perry escorted him to his cabin.

"Now what can I do for you?" the lieutenant asked once the men were seated.

"I have orders for you to seize the ship *Diana* now lying in Spanish waters off the island of Amelia, near the coast of Florida."

"Why?" was Perry's first question.

"The *Diana* left Wiscasset, Maine, flying American colors, but as soon as she reached Spanish waters the captain ran up the British flag and refused to return the ship to its owners. This warrant is for her capture."

"Is she armed?"

"Not to my knowledge," replied the marshal.

"Then it should not be so difficult to carry out the orders."

"There is one thing I haven't told you," said the marshal. "Not only is the *Diana* flying British colors but she is anchored under the protection of two British warships."

"Oh," said Perry, reading the warrant. Then he stood up. "I shall bring the vessel back."

No sooner had the marshal left the ship than the lieutenant began preparations for the expedition. To reinforce the *Revenge* he obtained three gunboats from Charleston and at once proceeded south.

The British ships lying alongside the *Diana* looked impressive, but since the arrival of the *Revenge* and the gunboats seemed to create no activity, Perry promptly went about his business. The crew of the *Diana* offered no resistance and so a prize crew was quickly put aboard her and the five ships began their trip home.

The United States lieutenant was just about to congratulate himself on the ease of his operation when the masthead sighted a sail aft.

"What do you make her out to be?" called Perry.

"British sloop of war, sir," was the reply. "She's crowding on sail, sir."

Every inch of canvas on the *Revenge* was ordered out and the signal made for the rest of the squadron to do likewise. Try as he did, Perry found the *Revenge* no match for the oncoming sloop and seeing that he was about to be overtaken he ordered a beat to quarters. The twelve guns of the *Revenge* would be no match, but at least they would provide some resistance.

Presently came a hail from the quarter-deck of the sloop.

"What ship is that?"

The reply was ready: "The United States schooner *Revenge*, Lieutenant Perry. Who are you?"

"His Royal Majesty's sloop of war *Goree*, Captain Byng. May we come aboard?"

Perry replied favorably and ordered the *Revenge* into the wind where she lay while a boat was put over from the *Goree*.

Presently a British officer came aboard and addressed the quarter-deck.

"Captain Byng would like to know the meaning of this convoy," was the message he brought.

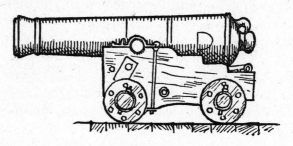

LONG GUN

Perry thought rapidly. This was the sort of situation that evoked the *Chesapeake* incident, but the *Revenge* was no match for the *Goree*. What the *Revenge* lacked in firepower she would have to make up in some other way. Under the present conditions the *Revenge* was at the mercy of the *Goree*. Given a little time he could at least better his position. He'd have to have that time. He'd make it by refusing to answer any questions.

"Tell Captain Byng that I see no reason to explain my business to him."

The British officer saluted and retired. As soon as he was over the side of the ship the lieutenant moved quickly. He ordered the *Revenge* about and into the weather position. Then he called for boarders.

"We're outnumbered two to one," he said to himself, "but perhaps we can take them by surprise." Then, convinced the *Revenge* was prepared to do her utmost if necessary, Perry signaled to the *Goree* that he was sending an officer aboard that ship. It might be that Byng was being unnecessarily overbearing; if not, then at least the *Revenge* was ready to put up the best fight she had in her.

While his longboat made its uneven trip toward the *Goree* the American officer inspected his own ship for last-minute preparations. He saw to it that the decks were sanded and that the wardroom was turned into a sick bay. Powder and shot were carried to each gun and the gun crews stripped to the waist and tied their handkerchiefs about their heads. Meanwhile the officer Perry had sent aboard the *Goree* was explaining the *Diana* business in great detail as instructed by his commander. In fact the subordinate did his job so well that preparations on the *Revenge* were completed long before he reappeared topside of the *Goree*.

Perry waited patiently as the longboat made its return trip. Intently he watched the face of his subordinate for a clue of the outcome of his conference with the British. Then he had it, long before the longboat had reached the side of the *Revenge*. The young officer smiled and shouted, "There'll be no trouble, sir."

The commander relaxed, but did not leave his

post at the rail. He had a word of praise to offer his subordinate.

"Nice work," he said when the officer reached the main deck. "We were fully prepared long before the conference was over. You delayed things beautifully."

"Thank you, sir, but Captain Byng seemed to be in no hurry. I guess he realized he had us if he wanted us."

"Perhaps," mused Perry, "but somehow I think it would not have been as easy to take the *Revenge* as Byng presumed." The lieutenant seemed to lapse into thought as though he were still pondering what might have occurred if the two ships had met in battle. Then he brought his focus back to his own ship and said, "Obviously Captain Byng was satisfied with our story."

"Completely," was the reply.

With that Perry turned his attention to the business of getting his convoy under way again. He thought the incident was closed; while he realized that he might have been a martyr had the *Goree* decided to fight, he did not consider himself a hero.

But the citizens of the United States did. No sooner had the convoy made Charleston than the story of how Perry had stood up to a superior British force spread through the country.

One of the first to hear the story and to appreciate it most was Commodore Campbell, who was in command of the naval station at Charleston.

"That's the kind of spirit we're going to need," said Campbell when Perry went to visit him. "Mark my words. This country will be at war with England soon. We can put up with just so much of this browbeating."

The younger officer nodded. "And when it comes I want to be in a position to do something about it. For ten years now I have been looking for action."

The two officers saw much of each other while the *Revenge* was at Charlestown and during that time they talked of little else.

"As far as I can make out," said Campbell, "the British have more than one thousand ships. True, they can't use them all against us, but they have more than enough in these waters now to handle our fleet."

"There's one thing you overlook," replied Perry, "British sailors are forced into service. They will not fight as well as our men. Furthermore, I'm convinced our gunners are superior marksmen."

"That may be true," Campbell countered, "but you still cannot discount the fact that while Jefferson was making us build gunboats the British were adding to an already large number of ships of the line. Mind you, I'm not one to duck a fight, but, well, the outlook isn't too good."

CHAPTER TWENTY-EIGHT

Aground

COMMODORE CAMPBELL WAS NOT ALONE IN HIS opinion that war with England was imminent, and by August, every seaman and officer in the United States Navy was officially well aware of the situation. In a communication to all commanding officers, Secretary of the Navy Hamilton did not mention England specifically, but he had no need to do so. The words of the communication, which all commanding officers were ordered to read aloud to their crews, were sufficiently plain:

You, like every other patriotic American, have observed and deeply felt the injuries and insults heaped on our country by the two great belligerents of Europe; and you must also believe that from neither are we to expect liberality or justice, but, on the contrary, that no opportunity will be lost of adding to the outrages to which for years we have been subjected. Among these stands most conspicuous the inhuman and dastardly attack on our frigate Chesapeake. . . . What has been perpetrated may again be attempted. It is therefore our duty to be prepared and determined, at every hazard, to vindicate the injured honour of our navy . . . and you are to maintain at every cost the dignity of our flag; and . . . offering yourself no unjust aggression, you are to submit to none, not even a menace, from a force not materially your superior.

At the time Perry received this notice, the *Revenge* was again attached to the northern squadron of Commodore Rodgers with Montauk Point to Nantucket as a cruising station and Newport as a base. No assignment could have been better. There were no waters that Perry knew better; his closest friends, Commodore Rodgers, Captain Hull, and Lieutenant Lawrence, commanded the ships of the squadron and every time the *Revenge* made Newport, Perry was sure to find Elizabeth Champlin Mason at home.

But Perry did not allow himself or his men to become lax. If there was to be a war, the *Revenge* for one would be ready for it. Day after day he ordered target practice for his gunners. Day after day the gunners fired away at bobbing barrels and day after day they created more driftwood for the beaches of Long Island Sound. There was more to this business than marksmanship, as Perry well knew.

"It's a matter of teamwork," he confided to his junior officers. "There are nineteen commands necessary to fire a gun and the faster we can get our men to respond to those commands the faster we can fire our guns. Mind you, accuracy is important, but if we can train our men to fire more accurate shots than the British, we shall be in a position to subdue superior forces. It's not a question of pride; it's a matter of necessity. England has more and bigger ships than we, so it is up to us to make the most of what we have. Furthermore, I'm sure we can do it. Most British crews are drafted, while our crews enlist voluntarily. That is why I think we can get better teamwork. If we make the crew feel it is the best in the navy, it will go a long way to prove it."

The cruise of the *Revenge* was interrupted in December by an order from Commodore Rodgers to join the squadron at New London. Rodgers wanted the harbors at Newport, New London, and Gardiner's Bay surveyed. He knew that Perry, despite little formal education, had made mathematics a hobby and so he ordered the lieutenant to proceed to Newport at once and complete the survey of that harbor within a week.

But a howling northeaster came roaring out of the west and pinned the *Revenge* to her berth. Before she could move, orders to return to New London came.

The *Revenge* weighed anchor at midnight on January 8, 1811, much against Perry's wishes. He had hoped to wait until the weather became more settled, so for good measure he took aboard a native to serve as pilot.

It was well that he did, for the *Revenge* had scarcely pushed her nose into Long Island Sound when a good Atlantic fog began rolling in. All that night the *Revenge* slatted and pitched off the coast of Rhode Island. For Perry there was little sleep. He knew the coast well enough to know there was danger and he constantly checked the pilot for his course.

"I make us to be well offshore," the pilot assured him. "And I reckon we'd better stay there.

Then come daylight we should have no trouble fetching New London."

But daylight brought little comfort, for the fog was so thick one could scarcely see across the deck of the little schooner. Perry ordered the chains to be manned continually.

"Tricky currents off this shore," he remarked to the pilot. "You're sure we're well offshore?"

"Far as I can make out, we are, but it's pretty hard judging currents in this fog."

"That's what I was afraid of," replied Perry, and resumed his fruitless efforts to make out a landmark through the fog.

By two bells of the morning watch the men in the chains were picking up sand on the end of the lead. There was still sufficient water, however.

Then it happened. It was as though a mammoth giant had brought his hand up out of the ocean and grasped the *Revenge*. The shock knocked Perry to his knees. The effect on the rest of the crew was just as severe. Each looked at the other with the fear of the unknown in his eyes. Perry glared at the pilot for a second and then went forward to see what the damage was. Already a boat was being lowered.

"Looks pretty bad, sir," the second lieutenant reported. "We might be able to pull her off though."

"Very good," said Perry. "Please order out the rest of the boats and see that the anchors are dropped."

But try as they would they could not budge the *Revenge*. She was fast on a ledge—off Watch Hill, the lieutenant soon discovered. Then he continued to issue orders according to the book.

Eight of the heaviest cannon were thrown overboard in an effort to lighten ship. When that failed Perry ordered the masts cut away. Still the *Revenge* remained unmoved.

"The water in the hold is gaining on the pumps," a midshipman reported.

Perry nodded and turned to his first officer. "Abandon ship," he ordered. "Remove the men from the sick bay first. They are to be followed by the midshipmen."

The officers remained aboard.

"We can't save the ship, but we can save her gear," he finally decided. "Keep the gig alongside in case we have to leave in a hurry."

The order to abandon ship was given early in the afternoon watch and the rest of the day was spent in salvaging as much equipment as possible. Each trip would be the last, the lieutenant felt, for at any moment he expected the *Revenge* to split in two. Yet the little schooner held out against the attack on her hull by crashing waves of the Atlantic and everything movable was taken off her.

And all this while Perry's conscience was jousting with his mind.

Why had he taken the *Revenge* out in such weather?

Orders are orders, his mind replied.

Why, then, hadn't he taken the schooner farther out to sea?

Because the pilot had assured him they were well away from the coast, was the reply.

What will the Secretary of the Navy say? asked his conscience.

That was one question his mind could not parry. He had no idea how this accident would affect his career and no matter how much he tried to minimize the loss of the *Revenge* he could not shake the fact that it was the first blot on his navy record. The loss of a ship was not something to be taken lightly.

The trip to Newport that night was long, cold and depressing, but long before he reached his home, Perry had decided just what he was going to do.

"I shall ask to be relieved of my command until a board of inquiry can sit on the case," he told his father.

CHAPTER TWENTY-NINE

A Change of Status

WAITING FOR A COURT OF INQUIRY TO SIT UPON HIS case would have been much more irksome for Perry had he not had Elizabeth Champlin Mason to distract him. In fact, so well did she distract him that long before the court convened, he was considering marriage should the verdict be in his favor. With typical New England caution Perry kept his thoughts on the subject to himself, but vowed that should he be exonerated from the loss of the *Revenge,* he would immediately open a rendezvous at the Mason home and attempt to sign on the doctor's daughter as first mate.

It was not until early spring that the court rendered its decision. Perry learned the verdict from Commodore Rodgers and the minute he laid eyes on his superior officer, he knew that he had been acquitted.

Obviously pleased, Rodgers handed over a letter he had received from the Secretary of the Navy.

Perry took the letter and read first the portion of it which Commodore Rodgers pointed out to him.

"With respect to Lieutenant Perry, I can only

say that my confidence in him has not been in any degree diminished by his conduct on the occasion. The loss of the *Revenge* . . . will no doubt present to Lieutenant Perry considerations that may be useful to him in future command. . . . If there should be any situation in the squadron to which you can appoint Lieutenant Perry that may be consistent with his just pretensions, and not interfere with the rights of others, you will appoint him to it; if not, he is to be furloughed, waiting the orders of this department."

When he had finished, Perry said, "I suppose I should be pleased by this, but I am afraid I'm not. The loss of the command is more important to me at this point and I am fully aware that there is no situation open for me in the squadron."

"No," replied Commodore Rodgers, "I'm afraid there is no position at the moment."

The lieutenant was silent.

"Then perhaps," he said finally, "I should take advantage of this furlough."

"How?" asked Commodore Rodgers.

"By getting married."

Rodgers smiled. "By all means," he said. "But despite the fact that at the moment the navy has more officers than ships to command, I should suggest that you go to Washington and inform Secretary Hamilton of the situation so that you will not be given any other assignment until you are ready for it."

With the Washington trip out of the way, Perry returned to Newport to discuss the situation with

Elizabeth Mason. That he succeeded in convincing her of the advantages of being a navy wife is borne out in the fact that on May 5, 1811, Elizabeth Champlin Mason became Elizabeth Champlin Mason Perry.

For a honeymoon, the Perrys made a leisurely tour of New England, pausing in Boston before swinging up the post roads and toll roads of New Hampshire and Vermont.

Had he given the matter any thought, the lieutenant doubtless would have left his naval uniforms at home, for at practically every tavern at which he stopped he was drawn into conversation on the subject of a possible war with England. Had Mrs. Perry given the matter any thought, she too would have seen to it that his uniforms were left behind, for she soon learned that a naval officer of Perry's caliber was unable to keep the thought of duty out of his mind. And the feeling that war with England was near was continually thrust upon him by these New Englanders who depended so much upon the sea.

If there was a war to be fought, Perry should be back in Newport, preparing for it, and not wasting his time bouncing over the roads of New England.

CHAPTER THIRTY

War Is Declared

NEW ENGLANDERS WERE JUSTIFIED IN ANTICIPATING and fearing a war with England, for New England shipping was already suffering and would suffer even more if war was declared. France as well as England was seizing American ships, but England was also searching American ships for alleged deserters from the British Navy. But the cause of the war was only incidental to Perry. His thoughts centered on the fact that a war with England would be fought primarily on the Atlantic and that the United States Navy, neglected under Jefferson's regime, was no match for Britain's thousand ships of war.

For a whole year Perry lived as a private citizen in Newport. Then in April, 1812, he learned that war was to be declared. Congress had secretly planned to declare war and had passed a 90-day Embargo Act to prevent merchant ships and seamen from being captured in advance, but the news leaked out and merchants hurried to get their last cargoes to sea. Perry also learned the politics behind the pro-

posed declaration of war. The South and West were
the instigators and they were thinking not in terms
of a naval war with England, but were planning to
strike at England by invading Canada. Perry, being
convinced that the brunt of the fighting would fall

on the navy, promptly went to Washington in search
of a command at sea. His trip was in vain, principally
because the United States Navy consisted of only
five frigates, three ships, seven brigs, and seven hundred gunboats. Congress had authorized the building of four 74-gun frigates, six 44-gun frigates and

six sloops, but these would not be ready for some time. He had to be satisfied with the command of eight gunboats with Newport as his base. He knew that he would never make history with this station, but he also realized that if the complement of men under him was built into an effective organization it might prove a valuable asset in obtaining a more important command. Consequently, he lost no time in opening a recruiting station in New London as ordered and training his recruits as quickly as possible.

He was still at Newport when President Madison signed the declaration of war in June.

Then the men with whom he had grown up in the navy began getting the opportunities he sought. On August 17th the *Constitution*, Commodore Isaac Hull, whipped the British warship *Guerriere* in less than thirty minutes. The victory strengthened Perry's belief in the fact that marksmanship was the most important factor in the training of American crews. He consequently doubled his efforts in training his own men.

In September, Captain David Porter, in command of the frigate *Essex*, returned to Boston with ten prizes to his credit.

These victories caused Perry to do some thinking.

"If I am not to be given a chance to prove myself on the sea," he thought, "perhaps I may prove myself somewhere else. Where, is the question."

Perry's contacts in Washington supplied him with the answer. The invasion of Canada had proved a flop and now the British had taken the initiative in that area. They were in control of Lake Erie, had won most of the American Indians in the vicinity, to their side and were planning to drive down the Ohio and Mississippi rivers, cutting off the United States from the West. To stop this advance, the United States would have to gain control of Lake Erie.

Here was a real problem for Perry. The British Navy was too occupied by its war with France to spend much time in the western Atlantic. And much as he would have liked the command of a frigate he realized that the few United States ships at sea were in good hands. In adddition, he knew that United States privateers were helping the cause on the Atlantic. And the more he thought about the Erie situation the more important he realized it to be and the more he felt that here was his opportunity. Consequently, he put in a bid for service on the lake. Then he settled down to study. He wanted to have his plans fully prepared in case the opportunity presented itself.

Perry knew that the government had taken some action in the matter. Daniel Dobbins, a lake captain with a capacity for getting things done, was starting to build a fleet at Presque Isle on the southern shore of Lake Erie. Dobbins had sold President Madison on the need for such a fleet and, armed with $2,000 and nothing else, he started the job. He had secured Henry Eckford as architect and Noah Brown as shipbuilder. His only other assets were plenty of timber and a safe harbor.

As Perry studied his maps he knew that men as well as officers would be needed on the lakes; consequently, he wrote to Commodore Isaac Chauncey, who had been placed in command on the lakes. Chauncey was stationed at Sackets Harbor on Lake Ontario and Perry felt that Chauncey would have all he could do to handle the affairs on one lake and would welcome assistance on Lake Erie. Command at Lake Erie was just what Perry wanted, for he felt that there the decisive battle would be fought.

In October came a letter from the Secretary of the Navy. As he opened it he was disappointed and then as he held the papers in his hands his disappointment disappeared. It was not the orders he had expected, but rather his commission as master commandant. The more he fingered the commission the more he realized that here was an opening. The Secretary of the Navy was in a good mood.

The newly appointed commandant sat down and addressed another letter to Washington. The most esteemed secretary of the navy must realize how greatly pleased the master commandant was to receive his commission, but the secretary of the navy must realize also that the commission was of no use unless it brought its owner a chance to prove he deserved the rank.

The letter brought a promise by return post

that the writer would be given the first vacant command.

But time continued to drag on and while Perry waited in Newport his friends continued to make the most of their opportunities on the Atlantic.

On October 25th his close friend Captain Stephen Decatur of the frigate *United States* conquered the British frigate *Macedonian,* in a brilliant battle of an hour's duration in a rough sea.

Then, in December, Captain William Bainbridge brought more credit to the United States Navy and the frigate *Constitution* by defeating the British frigate *Java* off the coast of Brazil.

The new year came and still no word from Washington or Sackets Harbor. Perry looked again toward the sea. A rumor came to him that Captain James Lawrence was to be promoted to the *Chesapeake* and Perry wrote Washington asking that he be given command of Lawrence's present ship, the *Hornet.*

Like most of Perry's letters, this one remained unanswered.

If Perry ever regretted his decision to stick with the navy now was the time. For nearly fifteen years he had seen opportunities go to his friends and, it seemed to him, he was destined to witness the present conflict from Newport.

With the suddenness of a Narragansett Bay squall his luck changed. Three letters arrived in rapid succession. Commodore Chauncey stated he had asked that Perry be assigned to the lakes. Secretary Jones stated that he had granted Chauncey's request. The third letter contained his orders.

"Go with all the best men in your flotilla, and join Commodore Chauncey at Sackets Harbor."

CHAPTER THIRTY-ONE

On to Erie

PERRY WELL KNEW THE PRIMITIVE ACCOMMODATIONS he would find at Lake Erie, but his men, when told of the new assignment, looked forward to the change of scenery. In order to avoid as much inconvenience as possible for his men, Perry shipped them in groups of fifty. The first batch left February 18, 1813, on its long trek to the northwest under Sailing Master Thomas Almy. The second, in command of Sailing Master Stephen Champlin, went two days later; on the 21st, the third half hundred took off.

For Perry the departure was doubly trying for his wife had been waiting daily for the arrival of their first child. But Elizabeth Perry, having lived her whole life in a seaport, no doubt was prepared for just such a situation. Sailing men rarely fitted their careers to the needs of their families. So, on the dismal rainy morning of February 22nd, Perry set out in an open rowboat for the west shore of Narragansett Bay. He planned to spend the night in Lebanon, Connecticut, where his parents were now living.

At Lebanon Perry found almost the identical situation with which his father had been faced fifteen years ago. Perry's brother Alexander, now thirteen, wanted to join the navy and go to Lake Erie.

"No," said Perry. "If I were taking a command on the ocean I might consider the matter, but this assignment is too dangerous. The trip to Lake Erie will be hard enough without having to contend with hostile Indians and I don't want Alexander scalped before he has a chance to learn his trade."

Alexander, being of the same stock as his older brother, did not give up without a fight. The argument lasted most of the night and when Perry seated himself in the sleigh early the next morning, in preparation for the long trip to Albany, Alexander was beside him. During the night the rain had ceased and the temperature had fallen sharply. It was a cold uncomfortable ride to Hartford, which they reached around midnight. From Hartford the Perry brothers took a mail coach up the Connecticut River to Brattleboro where they changed for one going west to Albany. It took them three days to reach Albany and there they settled down in the tavern to await the arrival of Commodore Chauncey, whom Perry had never met.

But the commandant felt that he would have much in common with his superior for both men had been in the Mediterranean at the same time. Consequently, they lost little time in becoming acquainted when the commodore arrived three days later. At dinner that night Perry received the orders for which he had hoped.

"You are to relieve Captain Dobbins of the command at Presque Isle. It is a difficult assignment, but from what I have heard of you I think you can handle it. We have no ships on Lake Erie whatsoever, and it will be up to you to build a fleet as rapidly as possible so as to be able to meet the British as soon as the lake has cleared."

Then, as though by mentioning it the matter had been completely taken care of, Chauncey began talking about his own troubles. He too was building a fleet so as to be able to meet Sir James Yeo, commander of the British squadron on Lake Ontario, in the spring.

Early the next morning the trio set off by sleigh up the Mohawk Valley. Then began the most difficult part of the trip, for they soon had to leave the sleighs and take to the woods. Sleighs, when they could get them, could be used to cross frozen lakes but for the most part they had to supply their own locomotion. On the evening of March 3rd they reached Sackets Harbor.

Perry had known when he started that the undertaking was a difficult one but he did not realize until he reached Sackets Harbor, just how difficult.

"There is nothing on these lakes," Chauncey told him. "Every item of supply has to be brought overland through the woods by horses and I am really afraid that we will have killed every horse in the country before we get all the material we need here. It costs a thousand dollars to bring cannon from Pittsburgh and Albany. Flour is worth a hundred dollars a barrel by the time it gets here. Of course you may be able to obtain some supplies from Buffalo but I would not depend on it."

Perry prepared to leave for Lake Erie at once but was forced to stay at Sackets Harbor for ten more days because of a rumor that the British were planning to attack the place and destroy the vessels under construction. Perry's opinion of Chauncey was not improved by the delay.

In fact, by the time Perry left, his opinion of his superior officer had been definitely lowered.

Chauncey had kept nearly all the 150 men that Perry had sent ahead from Newport and Perry real-

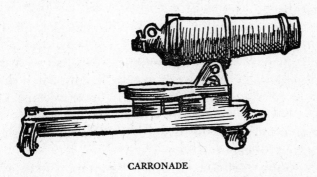

CARRONADE

ized that, though the men no doubt had helped him in getting his new assignment, he would have to do without their services.

It took eight days to reach Buffalo, where he stopped to make arrangements for supplies for Presque Isle. From Buffalo he started the hundred miles to Presque Isle by sleigh over the frozen lake. He stopped overnight at Cattaraugus Creek, where a chance remark made him more anxious than ever to get to Presque Isle. The innkeeper said that the British knew all about the fleet the Americans were building at Presque Isle and intended to cross the lake soon and destroy it.

Perry reached Presque Isle on the evening of March 27th and without stopping for dinner immediately called a conference of the men in charge of the building.

Dobbins, a small wiry man, impressed Perry at once.

Here is the man, thought the commandant, who not only had the energy to go all the way to Washington, but also had the ability to sell the president the idea of building the fleet on Lake Erie. I can depend on him.

Noah Brown, the shipbuilder, had been at Presque Isle for only a few days and so it was Dobbins who served as spokesman for the group. As soon as the lake captain had reported on the progress of the building, Perry immediately asked what precautions had been taken to defend the ships from possible attack by the British.

"I have had trouble enough to get men to build the boats," said Dobbins, "without thinking of protecting the fleet. We have got about sixty volunteers who would be willing to put up an argument, provided they had guns or ammunition."

Dobbins had a one-track mind and it was intent upon building the ships. No arrangements had been made for rigging or for cannons but the keels of two brigs and a schooner had been laid while two other schooners were nearly planked.

Perry immediately sized up the situation. The first thing he would have to do would be to protect the ships. Then he would have to concern himself with the fitting out of his fleet. The building of it he felt he could leave in the capable hands of Noah Brown.

CHAPTER THIRTY-TWO

Trials and Tribulations

LONG BEFORE BREAKFAST, PERRY MADE AN INSPECTION
trip of Erie and what he saw did not improve his
appetite. Dobbins had transformed oak, chestnut and
pine trees from along the shore of the lake into parts
of five ships. From that good, but meager beginning the new commander would have to build, rig,
equip, supply, man and protect a fleet capable of
defeating an already superior British fleet. And all
this had to be accomplished by the time the ice went
out from Lake Erie.

Completely forgetting breakfast Perry called
Dobbins and Brown to the improvised office he had
taken in the tavern.

"The situation is worse than I had expected,"
the commandant said in opening the conference.
"Mind you, I'm not finding fault, but only this
morning did I realize fully the obstacles you men
have been facing. We have many things to do at
once, but we must have help. First of all we need
men to protect the fleet from enemy attack and
enemy spies. I'll take care of that. Secondly, we have
got to have carpenters and blacksmiths if we ever
expect to get the fleet ready by spring. Brown, how
many carpenters do you need?"

"Well, sir, I figure it's a question of how many you can get. I can use five hundred if you can get them. The more carpenters the sooner we'll get the job done."

Perry rubbed his hand across his forehead before answering. "I can't guarantee five hundred," he finally said, "but I'll try to get as many as I can. Blacksmiths too. Now, Dobbins, I'm going to use you for my assistant. We need guns, powder, shot, rigging, iron and seamen. I want you to go to the navy depot at Black Rock and don't come back until you have everything we need. I'll give you a list and an order. Meanwhile I shall go to Pittsburgh for carpenters and any supplies I can beg, borrow or steal. Don't worry about duplicating orders. We'll be able to use all the supplies we can get."

The commandant checked several items off the list he had before him and then turned to Brown again.

"There is one more thing I want you to do," he said. "The stockade and the three small block-houses overlooking the ships must be restored. I don't care if you do have to sacrifice progress on the ships. I want those fortifications put in order. I'm sure if I were the British commander I would see to it that this fleet was destroyed before it ever floated. Is that clear?"

Brown nodded.

"Good," said Perry, smiling, "I'd appreciate it if you would start work this minute."

When Brown had gone the commandant hurriedly gave Dobbins instructions for his trip to Black

Rock. Then he was off in search of men to guard his fleet.

For a week Perry scarcely slept, so busy was he in organizing the work of the fleet. In fact, he completely forgot his proposed trip to Pittsburgh until Sailing Master William Taylor of Newport arrived with twenty seamen. It was the first bit of encouragement the commander had received.

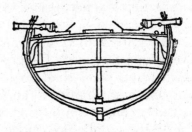

CROSS SECTION, SLOOP OF WAR

"Taylor," he shouted on seeing his old friend, "you're manna from heaven! Come have a drink. I've got a job for you."

Once inside the tavern Perry pumped his former neighbor for news from home and then outlined the situation at Erie.

"And so," he concluded, "I want to put you in command here so I can go to Pittsburgh. Your twenty seamen plus the two hundred militia I have been able to scare up should be enough protection for the moment. I'm really worried more about the fleet being burned than destroyed by attack. I suggest you keep a heavier guard at night."

With that he left his friend and began preparations for his trip.

Had Perry been a less determined man, that trip to Pittsburgh would have discouraged him completely. He found carpenters, sitting in a tavern. Furthermore, they were carpenters ordered to Erie by the Secretary of the Navy.

"Then what are you doing wasting your time here?" the officer demanded of the leader.

"Well, sir," the man replied hesitantly, "we didn't think there was much sense of our going to Erie without tools."

"Well, where are your tools?"

"We don't know. We came from Philadelphia by land and we were told our tools would be shipped by water, but they haven't arrived yet."

Perry sighed. Then he pulled himself together. "All right, men," he said. "You get to Erie as fast as you can. We'll worry about the tools later. There's work to be done."

Then he left the tavern in search of guns, but like the carpenters' tools, guns were not to be found. Nor could he locate any of the blacksmiths and blockmakers who were supposed to have been sent from Philadelphia. The best he could do was to beg four small field guns and a few muskets from an officer in charge of the army ordnance depot. All the other vital materials needed for his fleet he had to order.

It was with little enthusiasm that the commander returned to Erie and there he found an equally discouraged Dobbins.

"There's the net result of my trip," said the lake captain, pointing to a 12-pound cannon overlooking the fleet, "and it took me seven days to drag it a hundred miles."

Perry stared at the cannon a long time. Then he muttered, "We'll still do it," and plunged back to work.

But with all his problems unsolved the commandant soon was faced with another. The carpenters went on strike. They refused to work unless the food improved. Perry called in Noah Brown.

"How serious is this business?" he asked.

"The men are pretty mad," replied Brown, "and I can't say that I blame them a great deal. They are not used to the skimpy supplies we have."

"But you know as well as I do that food is hard to get here."

Brown admitted he did.

"Do you think that if the men realized the situation they might go back to work?" asked Perry.

"Yes, I think they would," said Brown.

"All right," said the commandant. "Pick out the ringleaders and tell them to go out and buy all the food they can get. I'll pay for anything they can lay their hands on."

Five days later three footsore carpenters returned to Erie empty-handed. The rest of the carpenters, seeing the impossibility of the situation, proved suddenly reasonable and went back to work.

No sooner had this problem been solved than another took its place. The ice went out of Lake Erie, leaving the unfinished fleet at the mercy of the British, should they care to make a raid. The four field pieces which had been obtained in Pittsburgh and the one cannon which Dobbins had brought from Buffalo would be no match for the guns of the British fleet. Meanwhile, Perry's fleet was becoming more valuable. On the last day of April three schooners hit the waters of Lake Erie. The commandant promptly moved these down to Cascade Creek to serve as protection for the unfinished brigs. A fourth schooner was nearly finished.

But surprisingly enough no attack came and during the month of May Perry continued to push his men to the utmost. The ships were still without guns and Dobbins had lost two 32-pounders when hit by a gale on a trip to Erie from Black Rock. Sailmakers and riggers arrived from New York during the month but the officers and sailors whom Commodore Chauncey had promised were among the missing. Had the fleet been ready for action, there would not have been enough men to man it.

To complicate matters further, Chauncey informed Perry of an attack to be made on Fort George at the outlet of the Niagara River. If successful, the attack would release five ships which were hemmed in the river by the guns of Fort Erie. Perry left for Niagara in a small four-oared open boat on the evening of May 23, 1813, and twenty-four hours later arrived in Buffalo. He then continued on to meet Commodore Chauncey on Lake Ontario.

The attack, a rather one-sided affair, was successful, due chiefly to the barrage laid down by Chauncey's fleet. The landing party, of which Perry was to have been in command, had played no part in the attack and he consequently devoted his efforts to commanding the fire of the smaller schooners. The victory caused the British to retreat from the entire Niagara area so that Perry was able to add a brig, three schooners, and a sloop to his fleet.

BRIG

Clearing the British opposition was the easiest part of the job. It took Perry two weeks to pull the heavy vessels up the Niagara River to the Black Rock Navy Yard. Two hundred sailors and dozens of oxen were used to pull the boats the ten miles from Gonjaquades Creek.

At Black Rock stores were put aboard in preparation for the trip to Erie. The five ships were valuable; besides adding seven guns to Perry's command, they also served him as a lever with which he could pry seamen as well as officers from Chauncey.

But the ships and their precious guns still had to be got safely to Erie. Perry well knew that the British fleet would be informed of the intended departure of the American vessels and he realized that the ships would never get to Erie unless he outmaneuvered Captain Finnis, the British commander.

Then on the day he had planned to leave for Erie, Perry was forced to his bunk by an attack of fever. But his duty was obvious and despite his illness he called Dobbins to his cabin.

"I've been thinking," he said: "if the British learned I was sick they might feel that our trip would be postponed. Now if we spread the word around and then sail as planned we might catch them off guard. Do you think you can get the squadron to Erie safely?"

"Yes, sir," replied Dobbins. "I know this lake better than anyone, particularly an Englishman. By sailing without lights and by keeping to the middle of the lake I think we can slip by the British. They'll be looking for us along the shore."

Perry smiled. "That's good thinking," he said. "I think you can do it."

And Dobbins did, bringing the ships safely into harbor just one hour before the British fleet came into view.

CHAPTER THIRTY-THREE

The British Threaten

WITH THE BRITISH FLEET OFF THE HARBOR TENSION swept over Erie like a tidal wave. From housewife to housewife and from sailor to civilian and back again the rumor of a British attack traveled. En route it expanded. The British were going to burn the whole town as well as the American fleet. No one was safe. The Americans didn't have any guns or ammunition. All the British had to do was land and the whole town was theirs. The American sailors and soldiers were planning to retreat into the woods and give up the fleet. The carpenters had already left. The rumors became more fantastic as they snowballed. Then suddenly they dissolved. The British fleet sailed away.

But Perry realized more than anyone that there had been considerable truth in some of the rumors and despite his fever he forced himself from his bed and went back to work. There was much to be done. He had eight ships in the water and his two new brigs were ready to be launched, but he scarcely had enough men to man one of them.

Meanwhile, General Harrison, whose army depended on a victory over the British fleet, was urging him to hurry. The Secretary of the Navy, who assumed that a fleet could be built from a wilderness merely by ordering it, also was demanding action. He could not know that the men he had shipped to Erie via Sackets Harbor were being retained by Commodore Chauncey.

But they were not the only ones who were now bringing pressure. They and the country as a whole realized that the fate of the war depended on what took place on Lake Erie. Only the men at Erie could appreciate how desperate the situation really was.

On July 4th Perry had all his ships in the water, including his two brigs, the *Niagara* and the flagship *Lawrence*.

By July 25th the fleet was fitted out but Perry still had to get the two brigs across the sand bar at the mouth of the harbor. But he did not dare to do this until he had enough men to man the ships, for the British would, no doubt, attack as soon as he attempted to get the brigs into open water. In desperation he opened a recruiting office in Erie. But only about forty men were thus obtained, bringing his command to approximately three hundred men, or less than half the number he needed. The fact that he had no officers to command his ships was the least of his worries. Meanwhile it was learned that Captain Barclay, who had taken over the command of the British fleet, had launched his new brig, the *Detroit,* and had received additional men. Perry was tempted to go out and fight, despite his lack of men.

On the last day of July he was sitting in the cabin of his flagship with his mind virtually made up, when there came a knock on the door. It was Dobbins.

"The British fleet has cleared out."

Perry thumped his fist on the desk and stood up.

"Good. Order the ships to the mouth of the harbor. We'll put the brigs over the bar at once. This is our chance. And," Perry added half to himself, "a long chance at that."

By four o'clock the next morning the vessels had been moved and Dobbins had gone out to sound the water on the bar. His report was not encouraging.

"This offshore wind is piling up the water on the other side of the lake and there is only six feet of water over the bar when ordinarily there should be seven."

The commandant was silent for a second.

Then he said, "I hate to do it, but we will have to lighten the ships."

"I'm afraid so," agreed Dobbins.

"But maybe we should wait to make sure that Barclay is not tricking us. It may be only a feint to catch us with both brigs on the bar at once."

Perry decided to wait a day. Meanwhile he had plenty to keep himself occupied. General Mead, who had brought fifteen hundred militia to Erie at Perry's request, reported that his men were determined to go home.

"The men say that their crops need harvesting and that now the British fleet has disappeared there is no need for them to stay here," Mead explained. "I'm afraid I shall be unable to keep them."

Perry sighed. He was becoming calloused to such things. To add to his troubles, Dobbins reported that now there were only five and a half feet of water over the bar. But the commander was determined.

"We'll take those ships over tomorrow if we have to carry them."

Accordingly the next morning five schooners went across at daylight and took up positions at the mouth of the harbor. Then came the *Lawrence*. Perry and Dobbins well knew that there was going to be trouble; despite the fact that the wind had subsided, the *Lawrence* drew nine feet of water and getting her across the bar would be no easy trick. Nevertheless, Perry sailed the *Lawrence* down the harbor anxiously waiting for the bar to grind under her keel. It did, when she was halfway across. Then for three hours every man under his command worked to lighten the ship and the commandant drove them with the knowledge that at any moment the British fleet might reappear. Guns were taken ashore and placed in a position to be of use in case of attack. Ballast was removed in bucket brigade fashion as was everything else movable on the ship. Still the *Lawrence* remained fast. But Dobbins as well as his commander had anticipated this and promptly two "camels," long airtight boxes, so designed that water could be pumped in and out, were moved alongside the *Lawrence*. Ropes and spars were placed under the keel and then the camels on either side were filled with water. The ropes were tightened and the water pumped out of the camels.

The crews held their breaths. The *Lawrence* did not budge. The hawsers had parted. Again the performance was repeated, and this time the *Lawrence* was inched forward. For three anxious days and nights the men labored to get the flagship over the sand bar and at eight o'clock on the morning of August 4, 1813, they finally succeeded.

Perry had been fortunate in slipping past the British fleet with the five ships from Black Rock, but it could not be hoped that his luck would carry him through this situation. It didn't. Scarcely had the men lightened the *Niagara* in preparation for her trip across the bar than the British fleet hove in view. Nor had the guns of the *Lawrence* been replaced. It seemed that a whole winter's work was to go for naught. But the commandant was not going to give up at the mere sight of the British fleet. He had seven schooners, boasting only eleven guns, to fight five British ships with forty-four guns but he was not going to lose everything at the last moment if he could help it. Hardened as he was to adversity, Perry did not hesitate long. All the time he had been in the navy he had struggled for an opportunity to distinguish himself and now that the opportunity was within his grasp he swore to himself that he would not lose it. He ordered every gun to bear on the British fleet and waited.

One thing was in his favor. The wind which had been blowing from the east had swung into the west. As it did so, it caused both the *Lawrence* and the *Niagara* to turn broadside to the enemy. Perry waited anxiously, expecting momentarily to see puffs of smoke from the British fleet but they did not come.

"Do you suppose," Dobbins suddenly said, "that the British think we have got any ships over the bar? It might look so from out there."

"Of course!" gasped Perry. "And Barclay would have no way of knowing that we have dismantled our guns. Perhaps we will fool them."

SLOOP OF WAR UNDER FULL SAIL

Hopefully they waited. Then, as suddenly as it had appeared, the British fleet turned away.

"It worked!" shouted Perry and Dobbins together. "Barclay thinks we are prepared to fight!" The *Ariel* was promptly ordered out to reconnoiter. Meanwhile the rest of the men fell to work again on the Niagara. The change in wind not only had prevented the British from attacking but had also brought more water to the bar so that only one trial with the camels was needed to get the *Niagara* across. By midnight the fleet was as ready as it could be under the circumstances.

If the men thought they were going to get a rest after their labors of the past four days, they were mistaken. Sleep was of the least importance to the man who not only had built this fleet out of a forest but had done so virtually alone. His men were green, many of them had never even sailed, his officers were inadequate, and he himself had little experience in navigating inland waters. The time was short and he had to give his men as much practice as possible. At four o'clock the following morning Perry signaled to his fleet to sail. For want of men, the schooner *Ohio* and the sloop *Trippe* were left behind. Lieutenant Daniel Turner commanded the brig *Niagara* and Perry was forced to use a purser, Humphrey Magrath, as captain of the brig *Caledonia*. Acting Lieutenant John Packet had the *Ariel*, Sailing Master Stephen Champlin the *Scorpion*, Sailing Master Thomas Almy the *Somers*, Master's Mate A. McDonald had the *Tigress*, and Midshipman George Senat the *Porcupine*.

The time to strike had come.

CHAPTER THIRTY-FOUR

The Tide Turns

FOR A SHAKEDOWN CRUISE PERRY WENT IN SEARCH OF the British fleet. Across the lake to Long Point and then westerly along the Canadian shore the fleet swept until unfavorable winds caused it to reach for Erie again. Not a sail was seen.

Back at Erie, the commandant's problems seemed no nearer solution. He knew that his fleet was superior to Barclay's in everything but men; and now that he had his fleet, he could not make up his mind whether to risk it while undermanned or not. He knew that he would get no second chance at Barclay. The outcome of the battle of Lake Erie and probably that of the war must be settled once and for all at this time. It was a difficult decision to make and Perry made it. He ordered provisions and stores to be brought aboard the fleet in preparation for a longer cruise, this time to Malden, the base of the British fleet. By the evening of August 8th the fleet was ready and Perry went ashore with Purser Sam Hambleton to clean up minor details. Hambleton was one of his closest friends at Erie and he had to have someone to talk to. At dinner in the tavern the commandant placed all his problems before Hambleton as though he were seeking the advice of an oracle.

"I can still delay," he said, "in the hope of getting more men, but if I have not convinced Jones and Chauncey of my needs by now, I certainly am not going to do it in the next few days. You know as well as I do that this collection of humanity that Chauncey has sent me is scarcely worth the food we're putting into it. If Chauncey had only let me keep the hundred fifty Newporters I sent up here originally, I would not hesitate a moment. Two of them would be worth fifty of these so-called seamen. I tell you it's a hard decision, for the longer I delay the stronger Barclay becomes. His new brig, the *Detroit,* is in the water, but I understand he is having trouble getting guns for it. If I could meet him before the *Detroit* was ready, our chances of victory would be unlimited. On the other hand, the longer I delay the better my crews will be trained."

Hambleton, not knowing how to bolster Perry's spirits, did not speak. Then as though in answer to the problem, a midshipman presented himself with a letter. The commandant quickly opened it and as he read, Hambleton could see the light of victory rekindled in his eyes. Suddenly Perry bounced from his chair.

"Lieutenant Elliott is on his way with officers and men. I'll send a ship to hurry them along."

The commandant strode out of the tavern and Hambleton had difficulty keeping up with him. Back on board the *Lawrence,* Acting Lieutenant John Packet was ordered to sail at once with the schooner *Ariel* and intercept Elliott and his men.

On August 10th Elliott arrived with two acting

lieutenants, eight midshipmen, a mastermate, a clerk and eighty-nine men. He also brought with him a letter from Commodore Chauncey.

The letter completely dispelled the enthusiasm Elliott's arrival had brought. Among other things Chauncey rebuked Perry for complaining about the caliber of the seamen sent from Sackets Harbor to Erie; he also upbraided the commandant for dealing directly with Washington instead of through his superior officer. In short, Chauncey answered all his subordinate's letters in one.

Perry thought a long time before answering that letter, but a man in his position could stand just so much. After nearly five months of continual pressure, it was not unlikely his calm and confidence should be cracked. This was the breaking point. He picked up his pen and wrote, not to Chauncey, but to the Secretary of the Navy:

"Sir, I am under the disagreeable necessity of requesting a removal from this station. The enclosed copy of a letter from Commodore Chauncey will, I am satisfied, convince you that I cannot serve longer under an officer who has been so totally regardless of my feeling. The men spoken of by Commodore Chauncey are those mentioned in the roll I did myself the honour to send you. They may, sir, be as good as are on the other lake; but, if so, that squadron must be poorly manned indeed. . . . The commodore insinuates that I have taken measures to obtain a separate command. I beg leave to ask you, sir, if anything in any of my letters to you could be construed into such a meaning. On my return to this place in June last, I wrote you that the *Queen Charlotte* and *Lady Prevost* were off this harbour, and if they remained a few days I might possibly be able to intercept their return to Malden. I had no orders to act; and the only way of obtaining them in time was to write to you, sir, as the communication between Commodore Chauncey and myself occupied considerably upward of a month. In my request, I meant this as a reason for applying to you on the emergency instead of to the commodore. I have been on this station upward of five months, and during that time have submitted cheerfully and with pleasure to fatigue and anxiety hitherto unknown to me in the service. I have had a very responsible situation without an officer, except one sailing-master, of the least experience. However seriously I have felt my situation, not a murmur has escaped me. The critical state of General Harrison was such that I took upon myself the very great responsibility of going out with the few young officers you had been pleased to send me, with the few seamen I had, and as many volunteers as I could muster from the militia. I did not shirk this responsibility; but, sir, at that very moment I surely did not anticipate the receipt of a letter in every line of which is insult. Under these circumstances, I beg most respectfully and most earnestly that I may be immediately removed from this station. I am willing to forego that reward which I have considered for two months past almost within my grasp. If, sir, I have rendered my country any service in the equipment of this squadron, I beg it may be considered an inducement to grant my request. I shall proceed with the squadron, and whatever is in my power shall be done to promote the interest and honour of the service."

CHAPTER THIRTY-FIVE

Final Preparations

ONCE HIS ANGER HAD BEEN SATISFIED BY THE WRITING of the letter of resignation, Perry promptly forgot the whole matter and turned his attention to the job at hand, the forthcoming battle with the British.

First of all, he planned to visit General Harrison at Seneca on the Sandusky River and he knew that he might be intercepted by Barclay's fleet en route. He had to make preparations for that possibility. Planning would have been much simpler had Perry been able to depend on the information brought to him by his spies. For one thing, he was not sure just how many ships Barclay had. If the *Detroit* was in commission, that made seven, according to the reports brought to Perry, and it was the *Detroit* that gave Perry the most concern. She was a much heavier ship than the *Lawrence* or the *Niagara* and was so planked as to withstand the close-quarter fighting that Perry proposed to use against her. The reports indicated that the British had more long guns than the Americans but that the Americans had the better of it in the weight of broadsides. If Barclay intercepted the fleet on its way to Seneca, Perry planned to be prepared to close with the British ships as quickly as possible.

On August 12th the ten United States ships sailed in double column for Seneca and the commander of each ship was fully instructed as to which of the British fleet he was to engage, should there be a battle. The flagship *Lawrence* would tackle the *Detroit,* while Elliott and the *Niagara* would meet the *Queen Charlotte.*

Fortunately Barclay was not sighted and the four-day trip from Erie to Seneca gave the crews that much more time to drill with the guns.

The meeting between the navy and army leaders was a spectacular one, for Perry was a stickler for naval custom and Harrison was hoping to impress a number of Indian chiefs he had gathered about him. The British had not swayed all the tribes in that territory to their cause and Harrison wanted to strengthen the bonds with the twenty-six chiefs who leaned toward the American side. Harrison knew his Indians, for they were greatly impressed by the fleet's salute to Harrison and the accompanying ceremonies of the day. For two hours the chiefs scrambled about the flagship like so many schoolboys and it took considerable tact to get them ashore again.

Once the Indians left, Perry and Harrison retired to the commandant's cabin for dinner and a conference.

"I am pleasantly surprised by your fleet," General Harrison said, once the men were settled. "It is a much better one than I had anticipated."

"It would be better still," countered Perry, "if it were properly manned. Few of my men are trained gunners. If the ships were properly manned, I would be fully confident that we could whip the British under any conditions."

"My situation is somewhat similar," the General offered. "I too prefer more time to train my troops but I suppose every leader is confronted with the same problems. From my reports I feel that even Barclay is not too well off. But let us come to the point. What is our next move?"

"I would like to meet Barclay at once," said Perry, "and settle the control of the lakes once and for all."

"And what if you do not meet Barclay?" asked Harrison.

"Then I think it would be your move and I would support you in any way you desired."

"That's agreed," said Harrison. "If you do not meet Barclay within a given space of time, then I shall move against Proctor, using your fleet to transport my troops."

"On one condition," Perry interjected. "That I be given an opportunity to go to Malden and try to bring about action with Barclay."

Harrison spent the night aboard the flagship and the next morning the two leaders continued their discussion.

"No doubt," said Harrison, "you have been considering an anchorage for your fleet in this end of the lake and I should like to recommend Put in Bay. It is well-protected and it is the best spot available. It is landlocked on three sides and protected on the north by a large island. Supposing we inspect it today."

Perry agreed, and that night when Harrison returned to his camp at Seneca, Put in Bay had been chosen as the anchorage for the fleet.

Then once again the fleet set out after the British, this time to Malden. And this time the British were sighted, but the only satisfaction derived from the excursion was the chance to challenge the English fleet to come out and battle just as it had been challenging the American fleet for so many weeks. As the American ships sailed up the Detroit River, Perry could observe that Barclay's new brig was in the water, but he could not tell whether it was completely armed and rigged. The commandant was not too disappointed that Barclay did not come out, for conditions were not ideal for a battle. The wind was spotty and so as not to become becalmed under the guns of the British forts the Americans retired quickly to Put in Bay. It was fortunate that it did, for the fever which had harassed Perry and his men all spring and summer flared up again and spread from ship to ship so that even Dr. Usher Parsons had to be carried about in order to perform his duties. Perry was in his cabin for a week and possibly might have stayed there longer had not nearly a hundred volunteers from Harrison's army arrived to reinforce his crews. The note from General Harrison which came with the volunteers explained that the general had noted the fact that Perry had few marines with his fleet and that these men had volunteerd for the job.

"Most of these men are Kentuckians," Harrison wrote, "and none of them has been on a ship, but for sniping work they cannot be surpassed."

Perry was pleased to receive these reinforcements even if they did wear the fringed shirts and

leggings of the frontiersmen. That they had rifles and knew how to use them was more than could be said for many of his other men.

As soon as he was on his feet again, Perry sailed for Malden, but once again Barclay refused to accept the challenge despite the fact that his new brig, the *Detroit*, now appeared to be ready for action.

This time Perry returned to Seneca in order to

confer with General Harrison. Perry felt that Barclay would come out and fight when he was ready. Harrison was not so sure. He feared some action should be taken before winter set in and he favored a joint action against Malden. Perry hesitated.

"Malden is too well-fortified," he said. "And Barclay's fleet would be backed by the shore batteries. I feel confident that I can beat the British squadron in open water, but I don't think I could do it if it were supported by the shore guns at Malden. If the fleet were defeated at Malden, then the army would be defeated too, and we would have lost everything. On the other hand, if I could meet Barclay in the open water and defeat him, then your attack on Proctor would have a much better chance of success."

"Well, have you any alternate plan to suggest?"

"First of all," said Perry, "I would like another chance to met Barclay. He'll come out. I guarantee it, for any officer trained under Lord Nelson isn't going to run away from a fight. However, if it appears that no battle is to be forthcoming in a reasonable length of time, then we could move your army to Middle Sister Island." And Perry pointed out the small dot on his map located by the Put in Bay anchorage.

"From that island," the commandant said, "we could move your army to any point on the Canadian shore we desired and at the same time your army would be completely protected from attack."

Harrison studied the map for a moment and finally nodded his head.

"That's a logical plan," he said. "We still have some time before the dangers of winter threaten us and I am willing to wait a few more days in order that you might have your chance at Barclay. It is now September 2nd. I think we can afford to wait another week. At that time, we shall meet again and arrange for moving the army to Middle Sister Island."

Three days later, Perry's opinion of Barclay was confirmed. Three prisoners escaping from Malden brought him the news that Barclay was preparing for battle. The prisoners also brought him accurate information concerning the British fleet. There were only six ships, not seven. The *Detroit* carried 19 guns, 17 of them long. The *Queen Charlotte* carried 17 guns, three of which were long. The *Lady Prevost* carried 13 guns, the *Hunter* 10, the *Chippeway* one long gun and the *Little Belt* three guns. The figures showed that the British ships were superior at long range and Perry quickly computed the weight of his broadsides in comparison with those of the British. Despite the fact that nine American ships, not including the *Ohio*, carried only 54 guns to 63 guns for the six British ships, the Americans could throw heavier broadsides. It was imperative, then, that the battle be fought at close quarters.

Perry at once ordered Dobbins to return to Erie with the *Ohio* for additional stores and supplies and then spent the rest of the night making plans for the battle. The next morning he ordered his fleet to sail. If the British were coming to meet him he wanted plenty of room in which to maneuver for the battle. But despite a double lookout, Perry found himself in the Detroit River before the British fleet was raised. It was still anchored as it had been on his two previous trips to Malden.

Back at Put in Bay, Perry called a conference of his officers despite the fact that most of them, as well as himself, were suffering from another attack of fever. Only Usher Parsons, of the three physicians, was there, and he had to be carried to the conference. It was to Parsons that Perry directed his first questions: How many men were sick? How many men would be available for battle the next day?

"One hundred sixteen men are on the sick list, sir," said Parsons, "and very few of those would have strength enough to be of any service should a battle be fought tomorrow."

Perry turned to Elliott.

"Can the *Niagara* do herself justice the way she is manned at present?" he asked.

"If all my hundred fifty-five men were sound," said Elliott, "I would still be undermanned, but able to operate fairly effectively. The fever has cut the *Niagara's* efficiency considerably."

Then the commandant questioned the rest of his officers similarly about the condition of their ships. When that phase of the conference was over, he presented the figures concerning Barclay's fleet that he had obtained from the escaped prisoners. All through the conference the importance of closing with the British fleet as quickly as possible was reiterated and after discussing the orders of the day each officer was presented a copy of the same instructions in writing. The first sentence on each copy was the same: "Engage each your designated adversary in close action at half cable's length."

Finally, when Perry felt that the instructions were clearly understood, he went to his sea chest and withdrew a package. Returning to the table around which the officers were seated, he said, "As you men undoubtedly know, Captain James Lawrence was one of my best friends and his last words were 'Don't give up the ship.' That phrase has stayed in my mind ever since the Secretary of the Navy requested me to name one of my brigs for the captain. I have here the battle signal for tomorrow's action, if it comes. When this banner is broken out from the main royal masthead of the flagship, it will be the signal for action—close action."

The commandant then silently undid the package. In it was a blue banner eight by nine feet, with Lawrence's last words printed upon it in white muslin letters.

CHAPTER THIRTY-SIX

The Battle Begins

PERRY'S SLEEP WAS INTERRUPTED BY A KNOCK ON THE cabin door. As soon as he could rub his eyes open he ordered his visitor to come in. It was Lieutenant Dulaney Forrest, and Perry could see that he was much excited.

"The British, sir," the lieutenant gasped. "The masthead reports a sail to the northwest."

The news brought Perry to his feet.

"Thank you," he said calmly. "I shall come abovedeck at once."

Perry quickly donned his uniform and went on deck. The sun was just rising on this 10th day of September and Perry quickly noticed that conditions were not favorable for a battle. The wind, very light and unsteady, was from the southwest. To gain the windward berth in the coming battle the American fleet would have to beat its way clear of the two islands which lay between it and the British fleet. No sooner had Perry sized up the situation than he issued orders to that effect. Two hours later the six British vessels could be clearly seen from the flagship and the fleet was still tacking back and forth in an effort to clear the island. Then the longboats and gigs were ordered over and the most experienced men were put to the task of helping to pull the warships into open water. The harder the men tried the worse the wind became, and Perry soon became convinced that he was not going to be able to get his fleet where he wanted it. He turned to Sailing Master William Taylor.

"How long will it take to weather the islands?" he asked.

Taylor shook his head.

"It looks pretty bad, sir," he said, "the way this wind is behaving. I'm afraid it will take us most of the day."

"So am I," said Perry. "I am going to bring the fleet about and we will go to leeward."

As Perry issued his order, Taylor protested:

"If you do that, you will have to engage the enemy to leeward, sir."

"I don't care. To leeward or to windward, they shall fight today."

Taylor bit his lip. Was the Perry stubbornness going to trip its master? Then suddenly Taylor grasped his commander's arm and pointed to starboard.

"Look, sir," he cried. "The ripple on the water! The wind is picking up. Maybe it's going to change."

The two men stared in silence toward the horizon. There was no doubt that a puff of wind was disturbing the water; as they watched, the ripple began to spread.

"Look," said Taylor. "It is coming this way. The wind has changed."

Perry showed his excitement, too.

"And if she holds," he said, "we'll have the windward berth over Barclay."

They were right. Scarcely had the words left his mouth than they were tossed back at him by the first puff of the new wind. It was picking up from the southeast and the run to the western end of the island became a reach. In no time the fleet was clear of the islands and squared away for the run down to battle.

With the wind in his favor, Perry put his thoughts on the next phase of preparations. Would the British line of battle be as he had anticipated it? It was now the middle of the morning watch, the British fleet was still eight miles away. Until he could make out the positions of the British ships, Perry had to content himself with the routine orders for battle. Small arms, boarding pikes and cutlasses were placed within easy reach in case of boarding, ammunition for the guns was brought up, and the decks were sanded and sprayed for better footing. In the next half hour, the wind increased steadily and cut the distance between the fleets in half.

Once again Perry had to change his plans, for the British line of battle was not as he had anticipated it. Perry ordered the *Niagara* to heave to and brought his flagship alongside. He wanted to confer with Acting Marine Captain Brevoort who knew the British ships well.

"I make out that to be the *Chippeway* in the lead," said Perry.

"That's right, sir," replied Brevoort. "And the *Detroit* is next to her."

"Then the *Queen Charlotte* would be the fourth ship in line."

"That's right, sir."

"Very well. Thank you," said Perry. "We shall re-form our line. The *Lawrence,* which is to engage the *Detroit,* will take the lead, supported by the schooners *Scorpion* and *Ariel.* The *Caledonia* will come second, in order to engage the *Hunter.* The *Niagara* will be third in order to engage the *Queen Charlotte,* and the other schooners will follow as we originally planned."

When the conference was over, the commandant ordered the noon meal to be served at once, for it could readily be seen that action was not more than an hour away.

"And a double order of grog," Perry ordered as an afterthought.

Then he made a tour of the ship before retiring to his cabin to straighten out his papers. There he placed the ship's log and all his official communications into a package, to which a weight was attached. His personal letters he read over and tore up. From his sea chest he withdrew the blue banner which was to be the signal for battle and went on deck again.

The British were still out of range when Perry came up, for the wind had fallen off somewhat. He still had time to give his men a last word of reassurance and so he ordered all hands aft. There he showed them the banner and explained to them its significance, just as he had done the night before with his officers. This time his voice wavered slightly.

The magnitude of the situation seemed to strike him suddenly. Here he was, after six months of struggling and privation, on the verge of signaling his fleet, the fleet he had created out of a forest, into what might be the decisive battle of the war. And his own career stood in the balance. Despite the fact that he had been in the navy for fifteen years, this was his first real test. For only a moment did he hesitate, and then to his men he said, "Shall I hoist it?"

"Aye, aye, sir," came the reply, and the battle signal was ordered away.

To cover his impatience Perry made another inspection of his ship, stopping before each gun crew to offer a word of encouragement. Many of the men he knew personally, for he had distributed the ones from Newport as widely as possible so that each gun crew might benefit from their experience.

Shortly before eight bells, when the two fleets were almost within range, the wind flattened out and Perry began to have a tired feeling in his stomach. Three things made him uneasy. First, a natural nervousness which he managed to cover well. Second, the fact that four of the small schooners had fallen far behind and were nowhere near their British adversaries. Finally, Perry could see that he was going to have trouble bringing his fleet into close quarters with the British. As matters stood at the moment, the American ships were in perfect position to be battered by the long guns of the British fleet.

Then came the British signal for battle, a bugle call. Almost at once a puff of smoke appeared from the *Detroit*. The first shot had been fired and the men waited tensely to see if it would take effect. It fell far short of the *Lawrence,* but all too soon the flagship would be in range and would be unable to reply. Five minutes later the British gunners scored

first blood with their second shot which crashed through the side of the *Lawrence*. A seaman fell, and soon a pool of blood formed on the gun deck. A flying splinter had found a vital spot.

Now that the British had found the range, they began to make trouble for the *Lawrence*. Time and again they hit the flagship, but she was still in no position to respond. Perry signaled for the schooners

Scorpion and *Ariel* to open fire with their long guns and the first shot from the *Scorpion* hit the rigging of the *Detroit*. Then the *Lawrence* tried a broadside, only to see it fall short. The tempo of the British barrage increased and the *Lawrence* wallowed helplessly while her rigging was being cut to shreds. Slowly the blood of the first seaman mingled with that of the other men and of the officers themselves. For fifteen minutes the *Lawrence* was at the mercy of the British without a chance to reply. Again Perry ordered a broadside and this time the shot found the *Detroit,* but did little damage. But the flagship was getting nearer and nearer to its opponent and soon would be in a position to make a fight for her life. High above Perry's head the Kentucky frontiersmen were sighting down their long rifles onto the deck of the *Detroit*. Suddenly a yowl of delight pierced the air and Perry knew that at last the *Lawrence* had scored. As the flagship crept nearer the *Detroit,* the rifles above him and the cannonades beside him increased their fire.

But things were not going well for the Americans. Only the *Lawrence* and the schooners *Scorpion* and *Ariel* had come to close quarters. The rest of the fleet was almost out of the battle. Muttering to himself, the commandant sent an order down the line for them to come to close quarters. It was obvious that the *Lawrence* would stand the bulk of the British attack if the rest of the fleet did not come to its assistance.

The *Niagara* was still out of range of even the British long guns and Perry became more concerned

when the *Queen Charlotte,* which was to have been
the *Niagara's* opponent, suddenly moved up in the
British line and brought her guns to bear on the
Lawrence. Now the United States flagship was getting double the amount of damage and the commander soon found himself forced to call upon Dr.
Usher Parsons to send up any men he could spare
from below. Gun after gun was being wiped out and
scarcely a spot on the whole deck was not covered
with blood.

The combined attack of the *Detroit* and the
Queen Charlotte on the *Lawrence* gave Perry little
time to think about the rest of the fleet. His men
were being butchered—the men he had brought
from Newport, the men he had trained so rigorously.
Yarnell, his second lieutenant, had been wounded
three times by flying splinters but still managed to
keep to his post. Purser Sam Hambleton was down
below in the wardroom and lying beside him was
Lieutenant Brooks, mortally wounded. Only a moment ago Brooks had been standing beside Perry
when a shot struck him in the hip and spewed blood
and pieces of bone all over the deck.

"Merciful God, let me die!" Brooks screamed,
and then, seeing Perry, pleaded with him to kill him
so as to end the pain. And Perry, helplessly trying
to comfort the boy, wished in his heart that he
might do just that. Instead he allowed two seamen
to carry Brooks below.

Not all the men were carried below. Some were
killed instantly. One shot passed completely through
a seaman as he stood talking to his commander. For

two hours the *Lawrence* stood up against tremendous odds, but not a single man hesitated in his duty. Where one man fell there was always another to take his place. The action gradually became a race to see which would last the longer, the *Lawrence*'s men or her guns. Time and again Yarnell or Forrest would come to Perry and plead for more men and the commander finally found himself calling down to the wardroom to ask if any of the wounded had strength enough to pull a line. But the men outlasted the guns. Three seamen, badly wounded, helped Perry run out the last one and then stood by and watched their commander fire it.

Yet, throughout the battle, even as they did their duty, there was a doubt in the men's minds. Where was the *Niagara*? Why didn't she come and help? The thought was constantly in Perry's mind too.

But when the *Lawrence* ceased firing, the *Niagara* moved up. It was as though Elliott had been waiting for Perry to be killed so that he might take command. But Perry was far from finished. He called for Lieutenant Yarnell.

"I will bring that brig into action," he said. "Is the gig fit?"

Yarnell reported that it was.

"Very well," said Perry. "You will take command of the *Lawrence*. I'll leave it to your discretion to strike or not as it seems best. Now bring me my long pennant and the battle signal."

Armed with the big blue banner Perry clambered over the side of the *Lawrence* where four oarsmen waited with the small boat. The smoke of battle hid the craft as it got away from the shattered flagship, but as soon as it was in open water it drew the attention of the British. Bullet holes began to appear in the sides and oars, and poorly directed shot sprayed water over the oarsmen. Perry stood looking in the direction of the *Niagara,* until the shouts of his oarsmen broke through his concentration.

"Sit down, sir," they were saying, "or we won't row another stroke."

Realizing how silly he was to expose himself, Perry smiled weakly and obeyed their commands.

The lull in the battle had caused the wind to freshen and the accompanying waves helped to spoil the British aim. A combined sigh and cheer from the fourteen men left on the *Lawrence* arose when they saw their commander make his way up the side of the *Niagara.*

CHAPTER THIRTY-SEVEN

Victory

COMMANDANT ELLIOTT MET PERRY AS HE CAME aboard the *Niagara* and if the latter had not lost his calm by this time, he certainly deserved to, for Elliott greeted him with the question: "How goes the day?" Perry's reply, besides being terse and surly, was also automatic:

"Bad enough. We have been cut all to pieces."

Then he came down to business.

"Why are the gunboats so far behind?"

Instead of answering, Elliott said, "I'll bring them up," and with that he took over the boat which Perry had just left and began the row down the American line.

Then Perry began ripping out orders as fast as he could word them. Up went his long pennant and the signal for close action. Back went the *Niagara*'s main topsail. When the speed of the ship was checked, she was squared away before the wind in order to bear down upon the British line. Then all guns were double-shotted.

While Perry had been engaged in straightening out his fleet, the American flag on the *Lawrence* had been struck, indicating surrender, but as soon as the *Niagara* went into action the *Lawrence* returned her flag to the masthead. Perry caught the action out of the corner of his eye and muttered, "Well, Lieutenant Yarnell is still with me. He's willing to draw part of the British fire despite the fact that he can't reply."

It had been quarter of three when Perry took command of the *Niagara* and in eight minutes she was within cannonade range of the *Detroit*. But despite the fact that the British brig had turned and opened up a heavy barrage, Perry withheld his fire. He wanted that first broadside to be as effective as possible. At the same time he saw the *Queen Charlotte* coming out of line and attempting to pass under the lee of the *Detroit* so as to be in a position to give the *Niagara* a broadside. All eyes were on Perry as the men waited the order to fire. The commander hesitated as though he were lining up a pair of sitting ducks on Narrow River. Then when the *Queen Charlotte* was directly beside the *Detroit,* he gave the order to fire. The effect was even better than he had expected. The broadside ripped the *Detroit* to pieces and then smashed on into the *Queen Charlotte*. The smoke from the broadside prevented any survey of the damage, but by the time the *Niagara* had rounded under the *Detroit's* stern, Perry saw that the *Queen Charlotte* was in distress. Her topsails had fallen, putting her out of control and forcing her to run afoul of the *Detroit*.

With the two British ships thus entangled, the *Niagara* was able to blast them with little return. Meanwhile the schooner *Lady Prevost* and the brig *Hunter* had moved up to join in the attempt to stop the *Niagara,* but Perry was able to get away two broadsides that left the ships virtually dismantled. Continuing in a circle, Perry brought the *Niagara* in range of the *Queen Charlotte* and the *Detroit* again. One broadside was enough, for when the smoke had cleared Perry could see an officer waving a white handkerchief attached to the end of a boarding pipe. The *Queen Charlotte* had surrendered. By the time the *Niagara* was ready to blast the *Detroit* again, that ship gave up, too, and seeing that the two largest brigs had surrendered, the *Hunter* and *Lady Prevost* followed suit.

The schooners *Chippeway* and *Little Belt* had turned and were trying to flee, but warning shots from the *Scorpion* and *Trippe* brought both British schooners into irons. Perry turned back to give a swift survey of the condition of his own ship and saw that the hourglass by the traverse board was just running out. It was three o'clock. In fifteen minutes he had turned what looked like defeat into victory.

CHAPTER THIRTY-EIGHT

"We Have Met the Enemy"

PERRY SAT DOWN, FOR WHAT SEEMED TO HIM THE first time in a week. He was so tired he scarcely realized that he was sitting on a dismantled cannon —hardly the most comfortable seat on the ship. He glanced about the vessel and then out across the water to the hull of the *Lawrence,* which was drifting to leeward. This was the climax of his career. For fifteen years he had waited for such a moment. He had hoped for it first under his father's command on the *General Greene,* but the *General Greene's* only action, the bombardment of Jacmel, was of scarcely any account.

And it seemed to Perry that the *Adams* might have been considered an unlucky ship also, from his point of view, for certainly nothing of importance happened while he was aboard her. On the other hand, he had to admit that the training he received on the *Adams* under Campbell and Hull had served him in good stead.

The *Constellation* took no honors in the Mediterranean while he was on board. Nevertheless, she reminded him of Campbell and Rodgers and Decatur and Somers and Lawrence.

On the gunboats he commanded along the

southern New England coast Perry at least had been able to train some of the men who had helped him this day; and these same men had in some measure helped him to obtain the command on the Lake Erie station. And although he had been exonerated for the loss of the *Revenge,* he still felt that it was a blot on his career.

Even his own *Lawrence,* which he had seen transformed from the virgin timber of Erie, had proved an unlucky ship, and Perry wondered whether bearing the name of the *Chesapeake*'s unfortunate captain had been a poor omen.

It was a long time since Perry had first set forth on the *General Greene* and most of those fifteen years had been filled with disappointment. Yet he had had breaks in his favor, especially since he had been on Lake Erie, when he certainly needed them. First, he had, with the help of Dobbins, squeezed past the British with the five ships that had formed a vital part of his fleet. Then Barclay had been scared off just when Perry thought his newly created fleet was doomed. It was not an ill wind that swung the *Lawrence* and the *Niagara* broadside to the British fleet when Perry and his men were laboring to get them over the bar. The arrival of reinforcements, just when he had determined to meet the British critically undermanned, had helped to make up for some of his past disappointments.

And even today the fortunes of war had twice turned in his favor: once when the shift of wind gave him the advantage over Barclay, and again when the parting of the rigging caused the *Queen Charlotte* to run afoul of the *Detroit*.

It had taken a long time for Perry to find action and honor but now the British were broken on the lake and General Harrison would soon be moving to break them on land. The threat of invasion was over.

But there would be more time later for reminiscing. The details of victory were many. For one thing, he must send a report to General Harrison. Perry beckoned to a midshipman.

"I want you to deliver a message to General Harrison at Seneca," he said.

He looked through his pockets and withdrew an old envelope and a pencil. Then he placed his round hat between his knees for a desk. Now he was beginning to enjoy the fruits of his labors. He wrote quickly, as though he had long ago made up his mind what he was going to say:

Dear General:

We have met the enemy and they are ours: two ships, two brigs, one schooner and one sloop.

Yours with great respect and esteem,

O. H. Perry

CHAPTER THIRTY-NINE

The Last Battle

"THEM THAT HAS GETS," WAS THE WAY THE SOUTH Country folk explained Perry's new influence. Whereas the first fifteen years of his navy career had been a constant struggle for recognition, the last six years were to be in complete reverse. Once having been given the opportunity to distinguish himself, Perry was never afterward out of the limelight; not only naval authorities, but ordinary citizens as well, appreciated the importance of his victory on Lake Erie. Few, however, appreciated the work that had gone into the building of that successful fleet, but that was not important. The main thing was that the victory had stopped the British invasion threat and had made possible General Harrison's rout of the British land forces in the Battle of the Thames on October 5th.

Thus when Perry received permission to return to Rhode Island, he found himself not only a public servant but public property as well, and as such he was forced to abide by the wishes of the citizens and attend all the ceremonies planned in his honor. It was a long trip home.

Perry was twenty-eight years old when he defeated the British on Lake Erie and the possibilities of an even more outstanding naval career lay before him, but he and his naval superiors, who now counted on him so much, failed to take into consideration the allergy which plagued him all his life —fever. He triumphed over it at Erie, but six years later it triumphed over him.

It was fitting, but unfortunate that the government decided to send its national hero to Venezuela as a diplomat in 1819. Perry had personality and prestige and if anyone could settle amicably the differences with the South American country he could. But Perry also had an allergy, though if he gave it a thought he did not show it, for when Smith Thompson, the new Secretary of the Navy, asked him if he would care to undertake the assignment, Perry's answer was a prompt "Aye, sir."

Thus on June 7th, with the frigate *John Adams* as his flagship, Perry broke ground. The purpose of the mission was to seek restitution for vessels seized by the Venezuelans during their struggle for independence from Spain. It was understandable that a nation struggling for independence would capture vessels first and worry about their nationality afterward.

A month elapsed before the squadron reached the mouth of the Orinoco River, where Perry transferred to the schooner *Nonsuch* for the trip to Angostura. There toward the end of July he started negotiations.

By this time he had begun to wish he hadn't undertaken the job, for it was the height of the yellow fever season and he was having difficulty controlling his patience.

"I've had some experience in this climate," he confided to one of his officers, "and frankly I don't like it. If the fever ever gets aboard, we're in for a lot of trouble. I want every precaution taken."

Because Simon Bolivar was away with the Venezuelan Army, Perry had to deal with the vice-president, Don Antonio Francisco Zea, and the experience tested Perry's diplomacy. The vice-president was more interested in entertaining his noted visitor than in getting down to work.

Perry was patient until the fever broke out on board the *Nonsuch*. Then he wrote Zea that for the sake of his men he must leave as quickly as possible. But by the time the Venezuelan authorities had agreed to make restitution for the captured American vessels, five of Perry's men had died of fever and the ship's physician was sick.

Still it was impossible for the noted American to leave. There was to be a dinner in his honor. The captain surely could stay three more days for that. And then after the dinner the ceremonies of reading the republic's new constitution were to be held and surely the captain would want to be on hand for such a great event. There was no choice, but whereas Perry had asked that every precaution be taken for his men, he was not so careful himself. Daily he visited the sick bay of the *Nonsuch*. It reminded him of his two trips aboard the *General Greene* and he knew that unless he could get his men out of the tropics their chances of ever seeing home again were slim.

But orders came first. His orders were to make a peaceful settlement with the Venezuelan government and the success of his mission would be undermined if he made an abrupt departure now. In battle a man had a chance to fight back, but there was nothing to do here but grit one's teeth. For four days after the agreement was reached Perry did just that. Then finally the *Nonsuch* weighed anchor for the trip downstream, but it was too late. Perry had taken the fever.

Still his only concern was for his men. If the *John Adams* could be reached, there was a chance that the epidemic might be halted. But at the mouth of the Orinoco River the weather turned against them. The wind gave out completely and the tropical heat bore down relentlessly on the becalmed and infested schooner. Now Perry began to lose interest in things around him. Time and again his mind betrayed him. Sometimes he was aboard the *General Greene;* sometimes he was struggling to salvage everything possible from the *Revenge.* But mostly his thoughts centered on the Battle of Lake Erie and the fruitful years following it. Things might have been different had the battle come earlier in his career; he certainly would have had more opportunities to prove himself. It was strange how people were reluctant to give a man a chance to show himself and then, once he had been successful, it was equally strange how easily he could have his own way.

The events of his life passed before him, much as they are supposed to do when a man drowns, only with Perry the process was slower and fitful, for much of the time he was unconscious. There were many pleasant pictures, especially of the days following Erie: his prompt promotion to the rank of post captain; the public welcomes arranged everywhere he had gone; and in Washington, where he had sought and obtained promotions for the officers who served under him at Erie, Congress had ordered a gold medal struck in commemoration of the battle. On the way home he had been forced to stop at Baltimore and Philadelphia for receptions and dinners in his honor. Everything he asked for he received, as well as many things for which he had not asked. The command of the *Java,* a first-class frigate under construction at Baltimore, had been offered to him without hesitation. Before Erie he had had to fight to get a schooner. The *Java* brought back more vivid pictures. To prevent the destruction of the ship on the stocks by the British he had gone to Baltimore and thus had taken part in the unsuccessful attempt to catch the British fleet as it sailed down the Potomac, away from the burning capital. He had been forced to command a land battery from Fort McHenry in that engagement. A fellow named Key had composed "The Star-Spangled Banner" during the battle, he recalled.

Eventually he had taken the *Java* to the Mediterranean, for the Barbary pirates had gone to work on American shipping during the War of 1812, just as Perry had said they would. But as usual there had been no action. The show of force was enough to make the Dey of Algiers come to terms.

But all had not been pleasant in those six years after the war. There had been a controversy over the actions of Lieutenant Commander Elliott and the *Niagara* during the Battle of Lake Erie. It was an unfortunate and needless business, but Elliott had kept the matter alive, declaring that Perry had damaged his reputation by his report on the Battle of Lake Erie. Their differences never were definitely settled, for it was not until shortly before Perry sailed for South America that Elliott's bitter attacks on him finally forced him to prefer charges against the captain. Then there was the duel with Heath, resulting from what Perry considered insubordination and neglect of duty while Heath was in charge of the marines on board the *Java* in the Mediterranean. But Perry would rather not think about that. Duels were a poor means of getting satisfaction and it was a good thing the vogue for them was dying out. Too many of his friends had suffered unnecessarily.

Now he was suffering from another kind of duel—a duel with death. At times the heat was unbearable and then again at times he was oblivious to it and everything else. He was not afraid to die, but he would have preferred a more glorious end. This was not the line of duty he had envisioned, nor was the *Nonsuch* the type of ship for final words.

Perry did not know it, but there were to be no final words. He wanted to get back to the *John Adams* and his subordinates did all they could to get him there, but when the end came he was still aboard the *Nonsuch*. The *John Adams* was standing by, but her commander was too sick to be moved, and his flag was transferred from the frigate to the schooner.

Thus Oliver Hazard Perry died on his thirty-fourth birthday, August 25, 1819, knowing none of these things but satisfied that he had carried out his orders.

Captain Oliver Hazard Perry was buried at Port-of-Spain, Trinidad. In 1826 the U.S.S. *Lexington* was ordered to return the body to Newport, Rhode Island, and a burial service was held there on December 4th.

Bibliography

Barrows, E. M., *The Great Commodore*. Indianapolis-New York: Bobbs-Merrill Co., 1935.

Bell, Lt. Frederick J., *Room to Swing a Cat*. New York-Toronto: Longmans, Green & Co., 1938.

Brown, Arthur W., *Spirit of Oliver Hazard Perry*. Providence: William R. Brown Co., 1928.

Burr, Henry L., *Education in the Early Navy*. Philadelphia: Temple University, 1939.

Channing, George G., *Early Recollections of Newport*. Newport: A. J. Ward: Charles E. Hammett, Jr. Boston: Nichols and Noyes, 1868.

Chatterton, E. Kelby, *The Story of the British Navy*. London: Mills and Boon, 1911.

Clark, Thomas, *Naval History of the United States*. Philadelphia, 1814 (2nd ed.).

Cooper, James Fenimore, *Naval History of the United States to 1856*. New York: G. P. Putnam & Co., 1856.

——— *Lives of Distinguished American Naval Officers*. Auburn, N. Y.: J. C. Derby & Co., 1846.

Dobbins, Capt. W. W., *History of the Battle of Lake Erie*. Erie, Pa.: Ashby and Vincent, 1876.

Durand, James R., *An Able Seaman of 1812*. New Haven: Yale University Press. London: Oxford University Press, 1926.

Dutton, Charles J., *Oliver Hazard Perry*. New York-Toronto: Longmans, Green & Co., 1935.

Green, Fitzhugh, *Our Naval Heritage*. New York-London: Century Co., 1925.

Hazard, Caroline, *The Narragansett Friends Meetings*. Boston-New York: Houghton Mifflin Co. (Riverside Press, Cambridge), 1899.

Hazard, Thomas, *Recollections of Olden Times*. Newport: John P. Sanborn, 1879.

Hill, Frederick Stanhope, *Romance of American Navy*. New York-London: G. P. Putnam's Sons, 1910.

Hull, Isaac, *Papers of Commodore Isaac Hull*. (Edited by Gardner Weld Allen). Boston Athenaeum, 1929.

Knox, Dudley W., *History of United States Navy*. New York: G. P. Putnam's Sons, 1936.

Lowry, Lt. Comdr. R. G., *Origins of Some Naval Terms and Customs*. London: S. Low, Marston & Co., 1930.

Luce, Lt. Comdr. S. B., *Seamanship*. New York: Van Nostrand, 1863 (2nd ed.).

Mackenzie, Lt. A. Slidell, *Life of Oliver Hazard Perry*. New York: Harper and Bros., 1840 (Vols. I and II).

Mason, G. C., *Annals of Trinity Church*. Newport: George H. Carr, 1890.

Naval Documents Relating to the Quasi War Between the United States and France, U. S. Navy Department (Vols. I-VII). Washington: Government Printing Office, 1935.

Naval Documents Related to the United States Wars with the Barbary Powers (Vols. I-IV). Washington: Government Printing Office, 1939 and 1940.

Nordhoff, Charles, *Man-of-War Life*. New York: Dodd, Mead & Co., 1883.

Paullin, Charles Oscar, *Commodore John Rodgers*. Cleveland: A. H. Clark Co., 1910.

Pratt, Fletcher, *Heroic Years*. New York: H. Smith & R. Haas, 1934.

Updike, Wilkins, *History of the Episcopal Church in Narragansett*. Boston: D. B. Updike, 1907.

Weeden, William B., *Early Rhode Island*. New York: Grafton Press, 1910.